Counting On Coins

Authors
Linda Fawcett
Carol Gossett
Myrna Mitchell

Illustrator
Margo Pocock

Editors
Betty Cordel
Michelle Pauls

Desktop Publisher
Tracey Lieder

MW00632795

This book contains materials developed by the AIMS Education Foundation. **AIMS** (**A**ctivities **I**ntegrating **M**athematics and **S**cience) began in 1981 with a grant from the National Science Foundation. The non-profit AIMS Education Foundation publishes hands-on instructional materials (books and the quarterly magazine) that integrate curricular disciplines such as mathematics, science, language arts, and social studies. The Foundation sponsors a national program of professional development through which educators may gain both an understanding of the AIMS philosophy and expertise in teaching by integrated, hands-on methods.

Copyright © 2002 by the AIMS Education Foundation

ISBN **1-881431-98-3**
Printed in the United States of America

Table of Contents

I Hear
and I Forget,

I See
and
I Remember,

I Do and
I Understand.

Chinese Proverb

iv

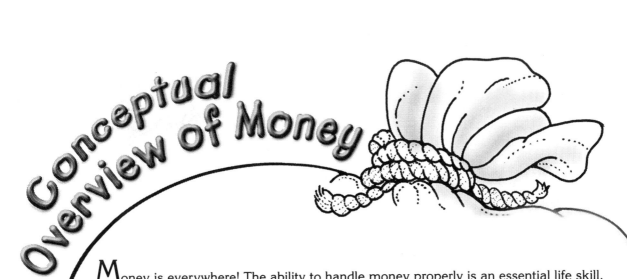

Conceptual Overview of Money

Money is everywhere! The ability to handle money properly is an essential life skill. Because children earn, save, and spend money, we have a responsibility to help teach them a basic understanding of it. The United States' system of coins makes that task difficult since it is somewhat counterintuitive. A dime is smaller than a penny, but its value is greater. Four pennies are worth less than one nickel.

Although money is a difficult concept for young learners, it is important that children have an understanding of money for the following reasons:

- it has applications to the real world where it is the basis of obtaining goods and services;
- money concepts are related to other mathematical concepts—for instance: operations, the decimal system, and fractions; and
- money concepts appear in most state standards and are often found on standardized tests.

Developing a Sense of Money

Primary children need multiple activities to gain the skills necessary to work with money. The lessons presented in this book offer experiences in which students will:

- identify and compare the values of pennies, nickels, dimes, quarters, half-dollars, and one-dollar coins and bills;
- determine combinations of coins for equivalent values and recognize that equal amounts can be reached through different coin combinations;
- distinguish between the quantity of coins and their values; and
- use coins in problem solving, real-life situations.

Through these games and activities, children will come to understand the importance of money and the role it plays in our daily lives.

History of Money
Money Through Time
Students will be introduced to the history of money by using buttons for bartering.

Explore and Sort Coins
Coin Talk
Students will sort coins by appearance (observable characteristics) and be introduced to the names of the coins (pennies through one dollar).
Coin Walk
In a format similar to the traditional cakewalk, students will march around a circle of coins. When the music stops, they will identify the coin they land on by name and appearance (heads and tails).

Conceptual Overview of Money

Pigs in a Pen
This activity focuses on learning the names and values of money and how to represent amounts of money symbolically. This is done in two formats: sorting coins by their various representations (heads, tails, cent notation, dollar notation, etc.) and using a coordinate system to locate different representations of the same amount of money.

Comparing Coin Values
Piggy Parade
Students organize coins based on value.
Coin Conflict
Students identify which coins have a greater or lesser value in a card-game format.

Exploring Equivalencies
Hundred Penny Pie
Students explore equivalent values of coins through the use of a circular area model.

Trading with Money
Bank On It
A gameboard format in which students will practice trading pennies for nickels. Extensions include trading nickels for quarters, etc.
Treasure Chest
In a treasure scenario, students organize a large number count by grouping sets of pennies and trading them or dimes.

Counting a Collection of Coins
Money Bags
Students will remove coins from a bag, and by using strategies such as counting on, they will determine the total value of the coins.
Coin Draw
Students will play a version of tic-tac-toe by totaling the value of three coins drawn from a sock and covering a space with that value on the gameboard.
Piggy Banks
In a timed situation, students will count coins and match collections of coins to their combined values.

Conceptual Overview of Money

Pocket Full-O Money
Students will add a collection of coins and examine different possible combinations with the same value.

Show Me the Money
In a shopping scenario, students will use coin pictures to show a variety of ways to represent specific amounts of money.

Making Change

Making Cents of Dollars
Students will exchange coins to equal specific values and count to find the total of a combination of coins. They will identify how money is part of their daily lives.

Who's Smart?
Students will make change along with the boy in a clever poem by Shel Silverstein.

Alexander's Not Rich Anymore
Using a piece of literature, play money, and calculators, students will keep a record of money as it is spent, making change along the way.

Books for a Bargain
Using a school book club order form, students will identify coins needed to buy items priced at $5.00 or less, and solve problems using money by estimating costs and making change.

Problem Solving

Shopping Spree
Students will play a version of tic-tac-toe by choosing different items to purchase that total the sum they want to cover on the gameboard.

Roll to a Quarter
Students will roll a die and take the number of each roll in either dimes or pennies. They will try to get as close to 25 cents as they can without going over.

Roll from a Dollar
Students will roll a die and subtract the number of each roll from a dollar in either nickels or dimes. They will try to get as close to 25 cents as they can without going under.

Magnificent Money Machine
Students will recognize number patterns and solve for missing addends using a milk carton and slide.

Conceptual Overview of Money

Riddle Me This
Students will listen to clues about coin values and determine what combination of coins would be used to solve the riddle.

Money in the Bank
Students will trade coins to find the fewest number of coins that can be used to represent a specific value in their "piggy bank."

Hot Dog Haven
Students will order from a menu, calculate the total cost of their meal, and determine how much change they should get back.

Additional Activities

Shake, Rattle, and Roll
These egg carton activities provide playful practice of coin identification, skip counting by 5s, 10s, 25s, and 50s, as well as the adding of two or more coins.

Ad-Ventures
Through the use of a variety of learning stations, students will identify how money is part of their daily lives. They will identify which coins, when combined, equal the values listed on coupons; compare amounts of money; and identify coins and the one dollar bill based on clues.

Dear Parents,

We are about to begin a math unit on money. The students will be engaged in a variety of money activities during the next several days. My goal will be to help your child learn to identify coins, figure the value of combinations of coins, and use coins to make purchases.

Multiple experiences such as naming coins, understanding how much each coin is worth, and how to figure out the value of groups of coins are extremely valuable for your child. Therefore, whenever possible, allow your child to count money–your spare change, his or her allowance, or other coins. Count with your child, starting with the coin that has the largest value.

Since children gain a better understanding of money when they work with real coins, I am asking each child to bring a collection of 50 pennies, 10 nickels, five dimes, two quarters, and one half-dollar (a total of $2.50). Thank you for your help.

Sincerely,

Money Facts

Penny

Obverse: Abraham Lincoln

Reverse: Lincoln Memorial, Washington DC

Special/Prior Editions: Between 1859 and 1909 pennies had an Indian head on the obverse and a laurel wreath on the reverse. The Lincoln penny, issued since 1909, originally had wheat ears on the reverse. In 1959, the reverse was changed from wheat ears to the Lincoln Memorial.

Trivia: The penny is composed of copper plated zinc and weighs 2.5 grams.

Nickel

Obverse: Thomas Jefferson

Reverse: Thomas Jefferson's home, Monticello

Special/Prior Editions: The Jefferson nickel has been issued since 1938. From 1913 to 1938 nickels had an Indian head on the obverse and a buffalo on the reverse.

Trivia: The nickel is the thickest of the four commonly circulating coins (penny, nickel, dime, quarter) at 1.95 millimeters.

Dime

Obverse: Franklin D. Roosevelt

Reverse: Torch with an oak branch to the right and an olive branch to the left

Special/Prior Editions: The Roosevelt dime has been issued since 1946. From 1916 to 1945 the design was a Winged Liberty Head.

Trivia: The torch on the back of the dime symbolizes liberty, the oak branch symbolizes strength and independence, and the olive branch symbolizes peace.

Quarter

Obverse: George Washington

Reverse: American Bald Eagle

Special/Prior Editions: The Washington quarter has been issued since 1932. From 1916 to 1930 the quarter was a Standing Liberty Type. In 1975 and 1976 special Bicentennial quarters were minted showing a Colonial drummer on the reverse. These coins are dated 1776 to 1976.

Trivia: From 1999 to 2008 state quarters are being issued at the rate of five a year which have reverses honoring each of the 50 states in the Union. These quarters are issued in the order in which the states joined the Union.

Half Dollar

Obverse: John F. Kennedy
Reverse: The presidential seal with the words "SEAL OF THE PRESIDENT OF THE UNITED STATES" removed

Special/Prior Editions: The Kennedy half dollar has been issued since 1964. From 1948 to 1963 the half dollar had Benjamin Franklin on the obverse and the Liberty Bell on the reverse. In 1975 and 1976 special Bicentennial half dollars were minted showing Independence Hall on the reverse. These coins are dated 1776 to 1976.
Trivia: The half dollar is the largest American coin overall with a diameter of 30.61 millimeters, a thickness of 2.15 millimeters, and a weight of 11.34 grams.

Golden Dollar

Obverse: Sacagawea and infant son
Reverse: A soaring eagle and 17 stars
Special/Prior Editions: The Sacagawea golden dollar has been in circulation since 2000. In 1979, 1980, and 1999 Susan B. Anthony dollars were minted. From 1971 to 1978 the dollar coin featured Dwight Eisenhower.
Trivia: Sacagawea was a Native American who served as an interpreter and guide for Lewis and Clark from 1804 to 1806 during their expedition to the Pacific Ocean and back. The 17 stars on the reverse of the dollar represent the 17 states which were in the Union at the time of the Lewis and Clark expedition.

Dollar Bill

Face: George Washington
Reverse: The Great Seal of the United States
Special/Prior Editions: The dollar bill has looked as it does now since 1929 when the size was reduced from 3.125" x 7.4218" to 2.61" x 6.14". It was also at this time that the current portrait and back design was set.
Trivia: The average life of a dollar bill is 18–22 months, as compared to three years for a ten-dollar bill, and four years for a twenty-dollar bill.

Money Through Time

Topic
Money

Key Question
How has our money changed through the years?

Learning Goals
Students will:
1. acquire information about how our monetary system has changed over time, and
2. participate in the process of bartering by exchanging buttons for products.

Guiding Documents
Project 2061 Benchmarks
- *Numbers and shapes can be used to tell about things.*
- *Getting something one wants may mean giving up something in return.*
- *Raise questions about the world around them and be willing to seek answers to some of them by making careful observations and trying things out.*

NCTM Standards 2000*
- *Use representations to model and interpret physical, social, and mathematical phenomena*
- *Count with understanding and recognize "how many" in sets of objects*
- *Create and use representations to organize, record, and communicate mathematical ideas*
- *Communicate their mathematical thinking coherently and clearly to peers, teachers, and others*

Math
Whole number operations
  addition
  subtraction

Integrated Processes
Observing
Comparing and contrasting
Communicating
Applying

Materials
For the class:
  timeline pictures
  buttons, large and small
  The Story of Money (see *Curriculum Correlation*)

Optional craft materials:
  wide craft sticks
  12 oz. paper cups
  yarn
  tissue paper
  pipe cleaners
  air-dry clay
  plastic lacing
  pony beads

Background Information
The use of coins as money dates back as far as 630 BC, but even before that, societies had systems and methods for buying and selling. Before they had money as such, people bartered to get the things they wanted and needed. Barter is defined as the exchange of resources or services for mutual advantage and dates back as far as 9000 BC. Eventually, certain items came to be recognized as having specific values and were used to purchase goods and to settle social obligations, such as marriage dowries. Items that have been used as money throughout the world at various times include cattle, cowrie shells, feathers, salt, wampum, ivory, and tools. In some countries, items such as these have been used as money as recently as the 1960s. While these items may seem strange to children, they were not strange to the people who used them.

This activity will introduce students to both the evolution of money and the process of bartering without money. The students will participate in a class Barter Day in which the students will exchange buttons for goods that they have created.

Management
1. Explain that the exchanges in *Part Two* of this activity are permanent, and that they will not get their buttons back if they choose to exchange them with other children for items.

2. During the week prior to Barter Day, divide the class into groups of four and work with each group individually to create items for them to bring to Barter Day. Each child will need to make several of the same item. The group should make enough so that each child in the class would have an opportunity to purchase their item. Several suggestions are provided here:

- Make a game in which the children catch a stick in a cup by using a 12 oz. paper cup, two feet of yarn, and a large craft stick. Punch a hole in the cup just below the rim. Put one end of the yarn through the hole and tie it in a knot. Wrap the other end of the yarn around the craft stick and tuck in the loose end.

- Accordion-fold tissue paper to make tissue paper flowers. Twist a pipe cleaner around the center of the tissue paper to hold the flower together. Pull the folds of tissue apart to create a flower.

- Make yarn bracelets by braiding three different colors of yarn pieces together.

- Create necklaces from yarn and air-dry clay for pendants. To make the pendants, form a ball of clay and flatten it. Use a rubber stamp to put a picture on it—press hard to get a good clear image. Next paint it, then rub the paint off so only the grooves of the pattern retain the paint. Use a straw to make a hole in the pendant. When the clay is dry, thread a length of yarn through the hole to make the necklace.

- Use plastic lacing to make lanyards for whistles, key chains, etc. The plastic lacing and patterns are available at most craft stores and many department stores.

3. Prior to Barter Day, send home a letter explaining what will happen in class and the fact that students will need to bring 15-20 buttons for bartering. Encourage the students to bring a variety of colors, sizes, and shapes—the more unique the better. Require that all buttons arrive by a certain date. Based on the frequency of different types, sizes, colors, etc., discuss with the students how the values will be determined and then determine button values. The students may choose to have the larger buttons or unusually shaped buttons worth a greater value, etc.

4. The timeline is not all-inclusive. Your students may enjoy doing some research and adding to the timeline provided.

5. It is suggested that the students be paired up for Barter Day. This will allow one student to stay with their goods while the other barters for things for themselves as well as their partner. Since the items will be displayed ahead of time, the students can discuss what they would like their partners to purchase for them and which buttons they would be willing to trade for the item(s). Partway through the allotted time, the partners can exchange places so that all students are able to experience both sides of the bartering process.

Procedure
Part One
1. As an introduction to money, discuss how money is used to buy goods and services that we need.

2. Ask the students to try to imagine a world without money. Explain that money can take many forms, in our day and age when we think of money we think of coins, dollar bills, credit cards, and checks. As you mention these items, place the label *Money Today* on a bulletin board and place the pictures of the check, coins, etc. under it. Tell the students that in the past people used feathers, stones, beads, salt, shells, and other items as money.

3. Read or tell *The Story of Money*. As you discuss the different forms that money has taken in the past, use the illustrations provided to create a picture timeline showing how our monetary system has changed. Label these *Money in the Past*.

4. Ask the students to think about what our money will look like in the future. Have them draw a picture of what our money might look like in the year 2080. Allow the students to share the pictures and discuss the thinking behind their predictions. Add these pictures to the timeline under the label of *Money Tomorrow*.

5. Tell the students you are planning a Barter Day. Inform the class that bartering is the exchange of goods or services without money. Explain to the students that Barter Day will be a day where they will be using buttons for bartering. Tell them that they will be able to exchange buttons for goods. Give examples of bartering such as trading a piece of unwanted candy with a sibling in exchange for a desired piece of candy or offering to do a chore for a sibling in exchange for his/her share of the pie.

6. Divide the class into groups of four and over the next several days work with one group at a time to prepare items for bartering. (See *Management 2* for suggestions.)

Part Two—Barter Day Activity
1. On Barter Day, review what it means to barter. Have students display the items they have made on their desks and then let them walk around to see what other students have made.

2. Once students return to their seats, have them take out their sets of buttons. Review as a class the characteristics that were determined to make some buttons worth more or less than other buttons (see *Management 3*). Write these guidelines on the chalkboard as a reference for students. Also establish the fact that students do not have to buy

every type of item displayed, but that they can purchase no more than one of each type of item. This will allow everyone to have the opportunity to purchase a variety of items.

3. Demonstrate bartering techniques by selecting an item and offering the student some buttons. Encourage the student to barter with you for the amount and selection of buttons of his/her choice. This should get things rolling. Announce to the class that they only have 30 minutes to do the exchange. Announce when five minutes remain.

4. When time is up, discuss the lesson. Ask, *How many of you traded your buttons for the item you wanted most?* Compare their bartering experiences with what happened years ago.

Discussion
1. How does bartering work?
2. How many students didn't trade at all? Why?
3. Was there anyone who traded more than once to get the item of their choice?

4. List three examples of bartering you have been involved in (this can include the Barter Day experience).
5. What things were used for money long ago? Why do you think they were chosen?

Evidence of Learning
1. Listen for correct responses as you ask the students to recall forms that our money has taken in the past.
2. While they are participating in Barter Day, walk around the room and listen for comments that suggest students have an understanding of the process of the exchange of goods or services without the use of money.

Curriculum Correlation
Literature
Maestro, Betsy. *The Story of Money.* Clarion Books. New York. 1993.

* Reprinted with permission from *Principles and Standards for School Mathematics*, 2000 by the National Council of Teachers of Mathematics. All rights reserved.

Money Through Time

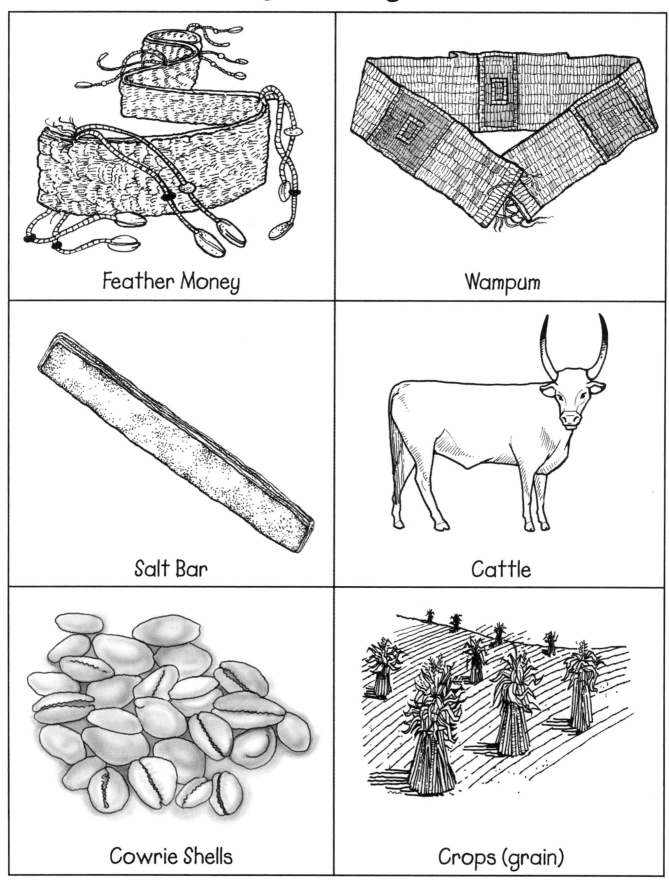

Feather Money

Wampum

Salt Bar

Cattle

Cowrie Shells

Crops (grain)

Money Through Time

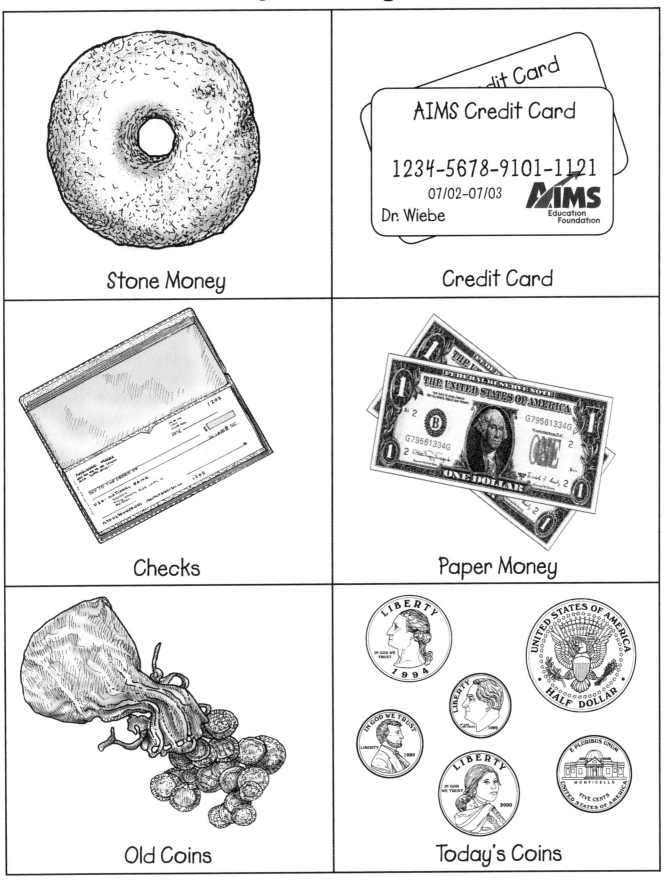

Stone Money

Credit Card

Checks

Paper Money

Old Coins

Today's Coins

Money Today

Money Tomorrow

Money in the Past

Coin Talk

Topic
Money

Key Question
What are some ways that you could sort these coins?

Learning Goal
Students will sort, identify, and name coins.

Guiding Document
NCTM Standards 2000*
- *Connect number words and numerals to the quantities they represent, using various physical models and representations*
- *Sort, classify, and order objects by size, number, and other properties*

Math
Number sense
  numerals
  number words

Integrated Processes
Observing
Comparing and contrasting
Sorting and classifying
Relating

Materials
For the class:
  coins (see *Management 1*)

For each group of students:
  set of money word cards (see *Management 2*)
  set of scratch paper squares (see *Management 3*)
  crayons (see *Management 4*)
  paper lunch sack
  hand lenses
  pocket chart

Background Information
A beginning step in learning about money is the identification and naming of coins. This activity asks the students to carefully observe similarities and differences between common coins used in U.S. currency. Many children enter school being able to identify and name pennies, nickels, dimes, and quarters. This lesson extends their experiences with half-dollars and coin dollars such as the silver dollar and the Sacagawea dollar. The lesson may be a review for some and for others an introduction to the actual names of the coins.

Management
1. Collect a set of at least 50 real or plastic coins including pennies, nickels, dimes, quarters, half-dollars, and coin dollars. Place this collection into a container.
2. Copy one set of *Money Word Cards*.
3. Prepare a set of 3" x 3" scratch paper squares. Each group will need six squares.
4. Gather crayons that have had the paper labels removed. The students will be using these to make crayon rubbings of the coins.

Procedure
Part One—Sorting by appearance only
1. Ask children to gather in a large group or at a center around the container of coins.
2. Give students hand lenses. Ask them to select coins from the container and to use the lenses to look closely at their coins.
3. Ask children to discuss with a partner how their coins are the same and how they are different.
4. Give each small group of students an assortment of 10-15 coins. Ask them to sort the coins into different groups and to describe the rules for their sorting.
5. Ask students to again sort these same coins into different groups and to describe the rules for this sorting.
6. Discuss what the students observed about the coins.
   - Some coins are silver.
   - Some coins are brown or copper colored.
   - Some coins have a picture of a man on one side.
   - Some coins have an animal on one side.
   - Some coins have a building on one side.
   - Some coins have a smooth edge.
   - Some coins have a rough edge.
7. Discuss what the students might use these coins for. Record their responses on chart paper.

7

Part Two—Introducing the names of coins

1. Conduct a quick survey to determine if the students know the names of the coins. If your students know the names of the coins, skip to *Part Three*. For those children who do not know the names, continue with *Part Two*.

2. Use an analogy to introduce the names of the coins:

   All of you are called students or children just like these are called coins or money. You also have special names: Karen, José, Stephen, Maria. Just like you, these coins have special names: penny, nickel, dime, quarter, half-dollar, and dollar. We can say that Karen is a student just like a penny can be called a coin or money.

3. Hold up one of each of the different types of coins, assigning the correct name to each one. Discuss the coins for which the students already know the names and practice naming the others. Provide several opportunities for the children to practice naming the coins.

Part Three—Connecting the real, representational, and abstract

1. Give each group of students a set of money word cards, paper squares, crayons, and coins.

2. Ask students to use the paper squares, crayons, and coins to make crayon rubbings of both sides of each type of coin in their collections.

3. Have students put the crayon rubbings of coins into a paper sack. Direct one child in each group to pull a paper square from the sack and to find a coin to match the rubbing on the paper. Have them give the appropriate name of the coin. Ask them to check with their group for accuracy.

4. Continue having the students take turns pulling out a crayon rubbing, matching to a coin, naming the coin, and checking for accuracy with the group members.

5. Introduce the money word cards.

6. In a pocket chart, place a set of the crayon rubbings of coins on one side and a set of money word cards on the other side.

7. Challenge a student to match the correct crayon rubbing with each money word card in a designated amount of time, such as ten or 20 seconds. Encourage the rest of the class to cheer for the student as the cards are moved into place on the pocket chart.

8. Repeat several times, allowing different students to have a chance at the challenge.

Discussion

1. Describe the coins you looked at using the hand lenses.

2. Explain some of the rules you used for sorting the coins.

3. What could you use the coins for?

4. What are the names of the coins?

Extension

Gather a set of coins from another country. Have the children compare the similarities and differences within these coins, and then between these coins and United States currency.

Evidence of Learning

1. Listen for accuracy while students identify and name coins.

2. Look for accuracy when students match crayon rubbings of coins to coin words.

* Reprinted with permission from *Principles and Standards for School Mathematics*, 2000 by the National Council of Teachers of Mathematics. All rights reserved.

8

penny

nickel

dime

quarter

half-dollar

dollar

Coin Walk

Purpose of the Game
Students will practice identifying coins by name

Materials
For the class:
large set of coins (see *Management*)

Management
Color, cut out, and mount the front to the back of each coin, and laminate to construct a large set of coins. Prepare at least one coin for each student in the class.

Rules
Game One
1. Gather students into a circle. Give each student a large coin. Direct students to place their coins at their feet on the floor.
2. Ask one student at a time to name the coin at which he or she is standing.
3. Have students turn so that they are facing the back of the person in front of them. As in the school carnival cake walks, start some music and have students slowly walk around the circle until you stop the music.
4. When the music stops, tell the children to stop as well. Go around the circle asking each student to name the coin next to his or her feet.
5. Tell the students who are standing next to pennies to jump up and down. Then tell the students who are standing next to nickels to turn around. Continue giving the students directions for each of the coins.
6. Tell all of the students to return to their coin walk position. Start the music again, having students walk around the circle until the music stops.
7. Ask students to name the coins next to their feet. Continue giving movement directions as before.

Game Two
1. Tell each student to hold one large paper coin.
2. Direct each student to find someone who is holding a coin just like the one he or she is holding.
3. Once all students have a partner, have them discuss the names of their coins and anything they observe on the coins.
4. Now tell students to find someone who is holding a coin that is not like theirs.
5. Once all students are paired with a new partner, have them discuss the names of their coins and things they observe on the coins.
6. Direct them to trade coins with their partners. Now have them find a new partner who is holding a coin just like theirs.
7. Continue the game for several rounds, giving students lots of practice naming and comparing coins.

Discussion
1. What are the names of the coins?
2. Which coin is called a penny? ...a nickel? ...a dime? ...a quarter? ...a half-dollar? ...a dollar?
3. Which coin is copper colored?
4. Which coins are silver colored?
5. Which coin is the largest?
6. Which coin is the smallest?
7. What did you notice was the same on some of the coins?
8. What did you notice was different on some of the coins?

11

12

13

Pigs in a Pen

Topics
Exploration of coins
Recognize coins by name and appearance

Key Question
What are some different ways that money can be represented?

Learning Goals
Students will:
1. match real coins to real coins (heads/tails),
2. match real coins to pictures of coins (coin rubbings), and
3. match real coins to value.

Guiding Document
*NCTM Standards 2000**
- *Connect number words and numerals to the quantities they represent, using various physical models and representations*
- *Sort, classify, and order objects by size, number, and other properties*

Math
Equalities
Number sense

Integrated Processes
Observing
Comparing and contrasting
Drawing conclusions

Materials
Pigpen handout
Sorting pigs

Background Information
Young children often struggle when working with money because they have been taken directly to the symbolic stage and have not had an opportunity to develop an understanding of what the money symbols represent. This activity focuses on having students learn the names of coins, their values, and how to symbolically represent amounts of money.

In the second part of this activity, students will apply the use of a coordinate system to locate the cards on a concentration board. It is assumed that children already know how to locate areas using ordered pairs. They should call out the locations of the cards by first calling the number of the column and then the letter of the row. For example (2, C).

Management
1. Copy one set of sorting pigs and pigpens for each group. Each group will need six pens. Put one of the following labels on each pen: penny, nickel, dime, quarter, half dollar, and dollar. The pigs and pens should be copied on card stock, laminated, and cut apart.
2. A real coin that matches the value of the pigs on the page should be glued to the blank pig on each page of pigs.
3. This activity can be done in either a whole class or small-group setting.

Procedure
Part One
1. Give each group one set of pigpens and sorting pigs.
2. Ask the students to spread out the pigpens on the table and sort the pigs into the appropriate pens. Make certain that all of the possible representations can be found in each pen. For example, one pig has the head of a penny, one has the tail of a penny, one has the name penny, etc.
3. When students have completed the sorting, discuss which pigs were placed in which pens and why. Question the students about where they might have seen the different representations for a penny, nickel, etc. [.25 can be found on store price tags, the words nickel, dime, etc. can be found on vending machines]

Part Two
1. Tell the class that they will be playing a memory or concentration game with money. Explain that there are several possible matches for each card just as there were several pigs in the same pens.
2. On the board draw a 6 x 6 grid. Label the bottom or x-axis with the numbers 1-6. Label the side or y-axis with the letters A-F. These labels should be placed in the areas between the lines and not on the lines. Place the 36 pigs previously used in *Part One* face down onto the grid. (The cards can be taped to the board or held in place by magnets or magnetic tape.)

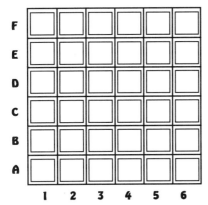

Extension

Have students match specific amounts of money represented in different ways. For example, two dimes and one nickel on one card, would match with five nickels on another card, etc.

Evidence of Learning

1. Check the pigpens to see if the students have accurately matched the different representations of the coin values.
2. Look for accuracy as the students match the pigs during the memory game.

3. Divide the class into two teams. Ask one student from the first team to call out a set of coordinates and turn the pig over that is in that location. Ask a second player from that team to call out a second location hoping to find a pig that will match in value. Play continues for the first team as long as matching values are located. When they do not find a match, it then becomes the other team's turn. The second team will call out locations until no matches are found. The game ends when there are no pigs left to turn over. The team with the most matches wins.

Discussion

1. Why were there so many possible matches in both the memory game and the pigpen sort?
2. What is another way of representing a penny? ...a dime? ...a quarter ?
3. How are $.25 and a quarter similar? ...different?
4. Where have you seen a quarter written as $.25?
5. Why do you think stores do not put pictures of money on the price tags?

Multiple Uses for the Pig Cards

- Turn over a card and match the picture coin with the real coin.
- Turn over three cards and order the cards from least value to greatest value.
- Draw two cards and write a number story with the values.
- Fold a 3 x 5 card in half to form the shape of a "v." This shape will be used as a *greater than*, *less than* sign. Draw two pig cards and compare the amounts on the pigs by placing them on either side of the *greater than, less than* sign in order to create a true statement.
- Draw two cards and add the coins.
- Play "show me." Call out a coin and have the students show the coin by holding the appropriate card in the air.
- Call out a value and have the students combine the coin cards to show that value.
- Turn over two cards and subtract the value of the lessor from that of the greater.

* Reprinted with permission from *Principles and Standards for School Mathematics*, 2000 by the National Council of Teachers of Mathematics. All rights reserved.

Pigs in a Pen

Pigs in a Pen

Pigs in a Pen

Pigs in a Pen

quarter

25¢

$ .25

Pigs in a Pen

half-dollar

50¢

$ .50

Pigs in a Pen

dollar

100¢

$ 1.00

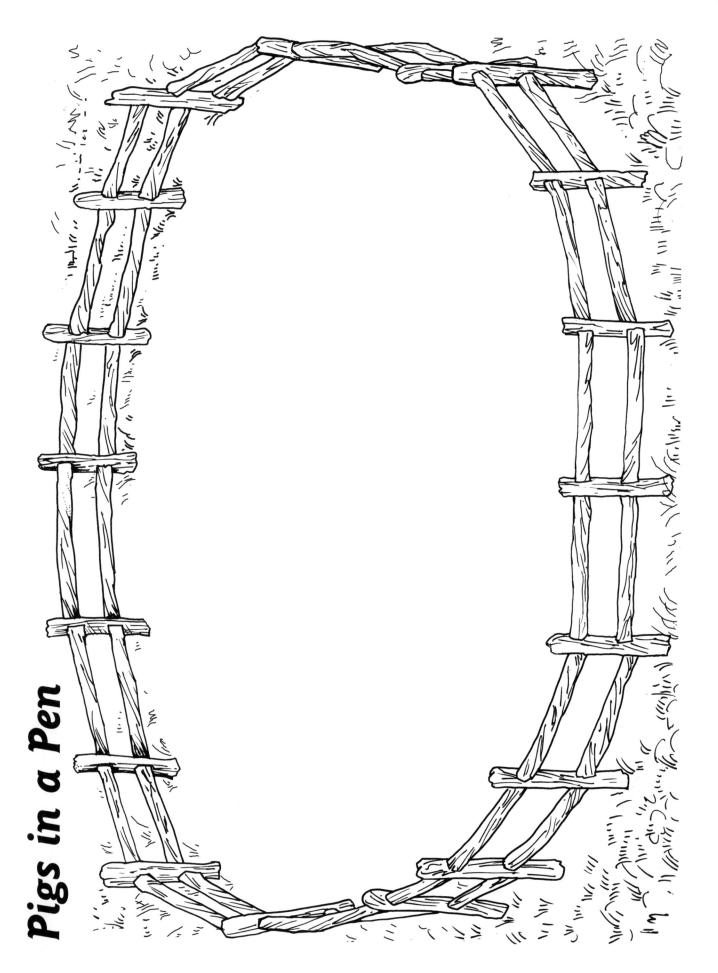

Pigs in a Pen

Piggy Parade

Topic
Money values

Learning Goals
Students will:
1. practice ordering coins by value, and
2. use problem-solving skills to order coins.

Guiding Document
NCTM Standards 2000*
- *Count with understanding and recognize "how many" in sets of objects*
- *Develop a sense of whole numbers and represent and use them in flexible ways, including relating, composing, and decomposing numbers*
- *Build new mathematical knowledge through problem solving*
- *Solve problems that arise in mathematics and in other contexts*

Math
Number sense
    more than/less than
Problem solving
Positional words

Integrated Processes
Observing
Comparing and contrasting
Communicating

Materials
For each student:
    Piggy Parade cards
    coins (see *Management 2*)
    paper bag
    yarn, 30 inches

Background Information
    This lesson offers students the opportunity to practice organizing coins by value. Ordering coins according to their values can also serve as an assessment of the young learners' understanding of coin values. Students are asked to order a group of coins from the least value to the greatest. In both parts of the lesson, they are given ordering situations that involve problem-solving skills. Positional words, such as *before* and *after,* are reviewed throughout the lesson.

Management
1. Color (or duplicate on colored paper) and laminate the *Piggy Parade* cards for extended use. Each student will need a set.
2. Each student will need a collection of play money that should include one of each of the following: penny, nickel, dime, quarter, half-dollar, and Sacajawea dollar.

Procedure
Part One
1. Give each student a set of *Piggy Parade* cards and a set of coins. Instruct students that they will order the coins on the line of pigs, from the least in value to the greatest in value.
2. Give students a paper bag and tell them to place their coins in the bag. Have them put their six pig cards in a row.
3. Have each student remove one coin from the bag. Explain that they will be placing the coin with the least value on the first pig in the parade line and the coin with the greatest value on the last pig. Tell them that they will need to make their own decisions as to where to place their first coin. Explain that they need to think about the fact that they will need to place one coin on each of the six pigs. For example, a student might draw a dime out of the bag, now he or she will need to consider the number of coins still in the bag that have a greater or lesser value before deciding where to place the dime.
4. Ask students to choose another coin from their bags and determine where it should be placed (before or after the coin already on the cards). Continue this procedure until all coins have been removed from the bags and placed on the cards in order from least value to greatest value.

5. Discuss specific coins in relationship to the other coins. For example, the dime is before the quarter in this parade line because the dime is worth less than the quarter. The dime is after the nickel because it is worth more than a nickel, etc.

Part Two
1. Divide the class into partners. Each pair of students will need a set of coins, one set of *Piggy Parade* cards, scratch paper, and a pencil.
2. Ask each group to place a dime on the first pig, a quarter on the second, a penny on the third, a half-dollar on the fourth, a nickel on the fifth, and the Sacajawea dollar on the sixth pig.
3. Have the students examine the placement of the coins and discuss what is wrong with the line up.
4. Challenge one student in each group to place the coins in the correct order from least to greatest value using the least number of moves. Have the partners use tally marks on scratch paper to record the number of moves taken. Compare the results and discuss strategies used by the different students.

Discussion
1. Describe the order of the coins in the least value to greatest value piggy parade line.
2. What is the order of the coins from greatest value to least value?
3. Beginning at ten, count on to 25.
4. Beginning at 15, count back to seven.

Evidence of Learning
1. Look for correct placement of coins according to value when students show their work on the *Piggy Parade* cards.
2. Listen for accuracy as students describe their coin placements according to value on their *Piggy Parade* cards.

* Reprinted with permission from *Principles and Standards for School Mathematics,* 2000 by the National Council of Teachers of Mathematics. All rights reserved.

31

Coin Conflict

Purpose of the Game

When comparing two coins, students will determine which coin has the greater (or lesser) value.

Materials

Set of coin cards (see *Management 1*)

Management

1. Copy one set of coin cards for each student. Have students complete their sets of cards by making rubbings of the coins of their choice (heads and tails) on the blank cards.
2. Children play in pairs.

Rules

1. The set of coin cards is shuffled, turned face down, and divided evenly between the two players.
2. Prior to the start of the game, the players must determine whether the card with the greater or lower value wins.

3. The first player will turn over his or her top card. The second player will then turn over his or her top card. Depending on which version is being played, the player with the greater (or lesser) value showing gets both cards. This continues until one player is out of cards or the allotted time runs out, at which time the student with the most cards wins.
4. In the event that matching coins appear, each player will turn over an additional card and the winner of that conflict will get all four cards.

Discussion

1. Which coin card was the best to have? Why?
2. Was there a card that you did not want to have? Why?
3. If you could make your own deck of coin cards, what would it look like?
4. How often do you think both players will turn over the same card? Explain.

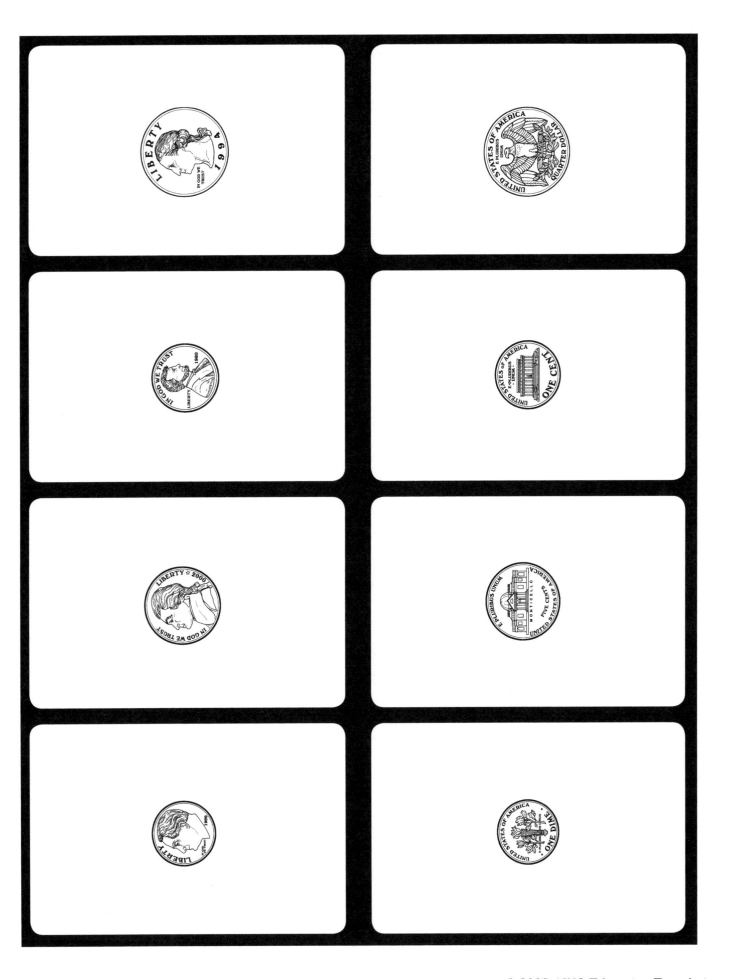

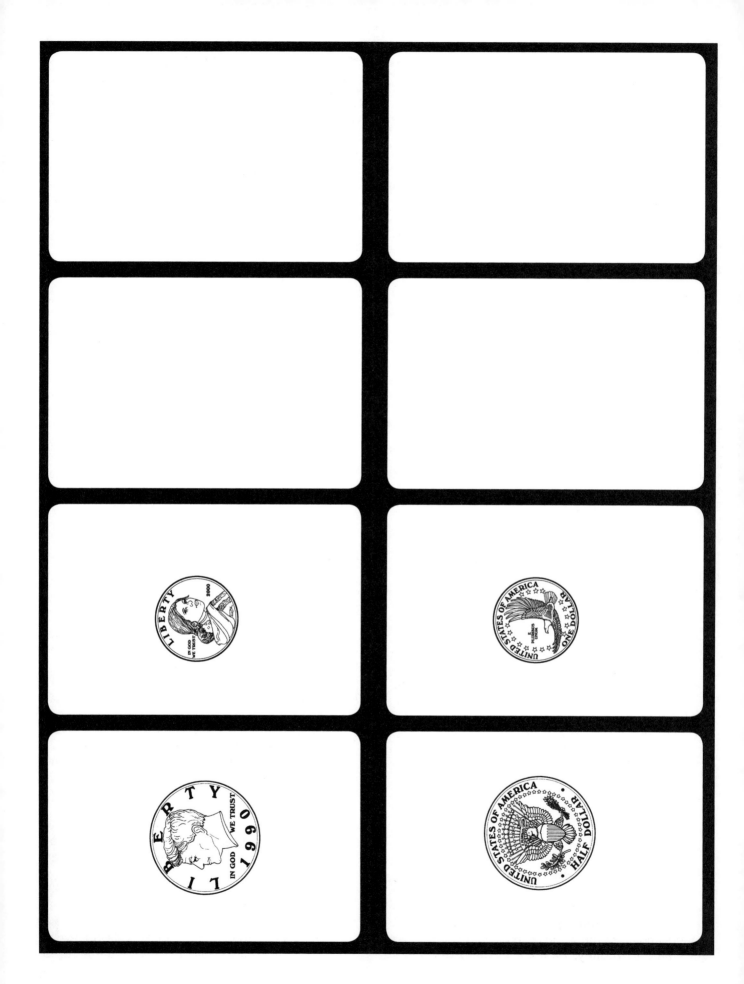

Hundred Penny Pie

Topics
Money values and equivalencies

Learning Goals
Students will:
1. use an area model of money values and equivalencies; and
2. understand a variety of combinations of coins that can be used to equal a nickel, dime, quarter, half-dollar, and a dollar.

Guiding Document
NCTM Standards 2000*
- *Count with understanding and recognize "how many" in sets of objects*
- *Understand the effects of adding and subtracting whole numbers*
- *Use a variety of methods and tools to compute, including objects, mental computation, estimation, paper and pencil, and calculators*
- *Model situations that involve the addition and subtraction of whole numbers, using objects, pictures, and symbols*

Math
Number sense
Skip counting
Equalities

Integrated Processes
Observing
Comparing and contrasting
Communicating
Generalizing

Materials
For each group of students:
  Hundred Penny Pie (see *Management 1* and *2*)
  colored paper *Coin Slices* (see *Management 3*)
  set of coins (see *Management 4*)
  set of money pictures
  scissors
  glue
  paper clips

Background Information
Young learners quite often enter school with a knowledge of money. Many can name common coins and paper money. This does not indicate an understanding of the value of money. When teaching the value of money, number sense is developed through counting, trading, addition, and subtraction. This lesson provides an area model for students to explore the value of money. By matching a one-to-one ratio of pennies to a dollar model, and then trading for fractional pieces of that dollar, students begin to construct an understanding of money values and equivalencies.

Management
1. Hundred Penny Pies can be purchaesed through AIMS, catalog number 4520. (Three pies, $9.95) You can make your own with the blackline masters that are included.
2. Duplicate on white paper and cut-out the *Hundred Penny Pie*. Construct the mat by taping four sections together to make a circle. Glue the picture of the Sacagewea dollar and the paper dollar to the back side of the penny mat and laminate. Prepare at least one mat for each small group of students.
3. Duplicate *Coin Slices* in five different colors of paper for each group of students. Use one color for the five-cent slices, another color for the ten-cent slices, etc.
4. Gather a set of 100 pennies, 20 nickels, ten dimes, four quarters, two half-dollars, one coin dollar, and one paper dollar for each group. You may wish to visit your local school supply/toy store and purchase play money instead of using real coins.
5. Duplicate a set of money pictures for each group.
6. This activity is divided into four parts, each of which is designed to be taught on a different day.

Procedure
Part One
1. Give each group of students 100 pennies and 20 nickels. Discuss how coins are money and that they can be used to buy things. Explain that the students need to learn how much each coin is worth so that they will know which ones to use when making purchases.
2. Explain that they can figure out how much each coin is worth by counting. Give each group a *Hundred Penny Pie*. Explain that this mat is a model of a dollar. Show the students a coin dollar.
3. Explain that this coin is equal to a dollar bill. Show a dollar bill.
4. Point out the small circles on the *Hundred Penny Pie*. Explain that there is one circle for every penny this dollar represents. Ask students to

place a penny in each of the circles on their mats. Direct them to count to discover the number of pennies in a dollar.

5. Once the students discover that there are 100 pennies in a dollar, discuss how it is much easier to carry around a one dollar coin or paper dollar bill than it is to carry around 100 pennies. Explain that this is why there are so many different kinds of coins. Instead of carrying around lots of pennies, we represent different amounts of pennies with different coins.

6. Give the students 20 five cent (nickel) slices and have them cut out each slice. Instruct them to place pennies in each circle on the slices. Discuss how each of these slices represents five cents, or five pennies. Explain that instead of carrying five pennies around, they could carry one nickel. Ask them to find a nickel in their coin collection.

7. If students are making their own penny pies, cut and paste a picture of a nickel on the back of each five cent slice of the mat. Discuss how each nickel is equal to five pennies.

8. Instruct students to place the nickel slice on top of a five-penny wedge of their *Hundred Penny Pies* with the pictures of the nickel showing. Have them use paper clips to hold in place. Ask students to count the number of nickels in a dollar by counting the nickel slices on the *Hundred Penny Pies*.

9. Have students count the nickels by fives to determine that they still have 100 cents, or one dollar.

10. Store the *Hundred Penny Pies*, leaving the nickel slices attached for a later lesson.

Part Two

1. Give each group of students the *Hundred Penny Pies*, 10 ten-cent (dime) slices, and a set of coins including pennies, nickels, and dimes.

2. Review the *Hundred Penny Pie* discussing how the 100 pennies and the 20 nickels are each worth 100 cents, or one dollar. Remind the students that it is easier to carry around 20 nickels that equal a dollar than it is to carry around 100 pennies.

3. Show students a dime and ask them to find this coin in their collections. Discuss how many pennies they think this coin represents. Have students cut out their ten-penny slices. Ask them to place pennies on the circles on these slices. Discuss how ten pennies equal a ten-penny slice.

4. If students are making their own penny pies, ask them to cut and paste a picture of a dime on the back of each ten-cent slice. Have them place these slices over the nickel slices and attach them using paper clips.

5. Ask students to count the number of dimes in a dollar by counting the ten-cent slices on the *Hundred Penny Pie*.

6. Have students count the dimes by tens to determine that they still have 100 cents or one dollar.

7. Direct students to lift the dime slices and count the number of nickel slices needed to represent a dime. [2] Discuss how it is easier to carry around two nickels than it is to carry around ten pennies, but that it is also easier to carry around one dime instead of two nickels or ten pennies.

8. Discuss how a nickel has the same value as five pennies, and that two nickels have the same value as ten pennies, and that one dime has the same value as two nickels or ten pennies.

9. Store the *Hundred Penny Pies* leaving the nickel and dime slices attached for a later lesson.

Part Three

1. Give each group of students the *Hundred Penny Pies*, four 25-cent (quarter) slices, and a set of coins including pennies, nickels, dimes, and quarters.

2. Review the *Hundred Penny Pie* discussing how the 100 pennies, 20 nickels, and ten dimes are all worth 100 cents, or one dollar. Remind the students that it is easier to carry around 10 dimes that equal a dollar than it is to carry around 20 nickels or 100 pennies.

3. Show students a quarter and ask them to find this coin in their collections. Discuss how many pennies they think this coin represents. Have students cut out their 25-cents slices. Ask them to place pennies in the circles on these slices. Discuss how 25 pennies make up the 25-cent slice.

4. If students are making their own penny pies, ask them to cut and paste a picture of a quarter on the back of each slice. Have them place these slices over the dime slices and attach them using paper clips.

5. Ask students to count the number of quarters in a dollar by counting the 25-cent slices on the *Hundred Penny Pie*.

6. Direct students to lift the quarter slices and count the number of dime and nickel slices needed to represent a quarter. [two dimes and one nickel or five nickels] Discuss how it is easier to carry around one quarter than it is to carry around two dimes and a nickel, five nickels, or 25 pennies.

7. Give students a chance to explore the many different possible combinations of coins that equal 25 cents. Have them remove a 25-cent slice from their mats. Ask them to rebuild the 25-cent slice using different combinations of penny, nickel, and dime slices. Discuss the results.

8. Discuss how a quarter has the same value as 25 pennies and the other combinations of nickels, dimes, and pennies they have discovered.

       36

Part Four
1. On different days, continue introducing the half-dollar and then finally the dollar in the same manner.
2. To make the 50-cent slices, cut out and tape together two 25-cent slices. You will need a total of four 25-cent slices to make two 50-cent slices.
3. To make the dollar slices, cut out and tape together four 25-cent slices.

Discussion
1. How many pennies equal a dollar? [100] ...half-dollar? [50] ... quarter? [25] ...dime?[10] ...nickel?[5]
2. What two coins equal a dime when combined? [two nickels]
3. What three coins equal a quarter when combined? [two dimes and one nickel]
4. Describe a combination of coins that can equal a half-dollar. [two quarters, five dimes, 10 nickels, etc.]
5. Why do you think we have so many different kinds of coins?
6. If I have a quarter and I need to change it in so that I have at least one nickel, what other coins should I also receive so that I still have 25 cents? [two dimes, one nickel; one dime, three nickels; five nickels, etc.]

Extension
Give students a variety of coin slices and have them explore the different combinations of coins they can use to equal a dime, a quarter, and half-dollar.

Evidence of Learning
1. Look for accuracy when students show their work on *Hundred Penny Pies.*
2. Check for appropriate combinations of coin slices on the mats.
3. Listen for accuracy as students describe possible coin combinations that equal a nickel, dime, quarter, half-dollar, and dollar.

* Reprinted with permission from *Principles and Standards for School Mathematics,* 2000 by the National Council of Teachers of Mathematics. All rights reserved.

Hundred Penny Pie

Make four copies for each *Hundred Penny Pie*. Glue a picture of the Sacagewea dollar and the paper dollar on the back side of the *Hundred Penny Pie*.

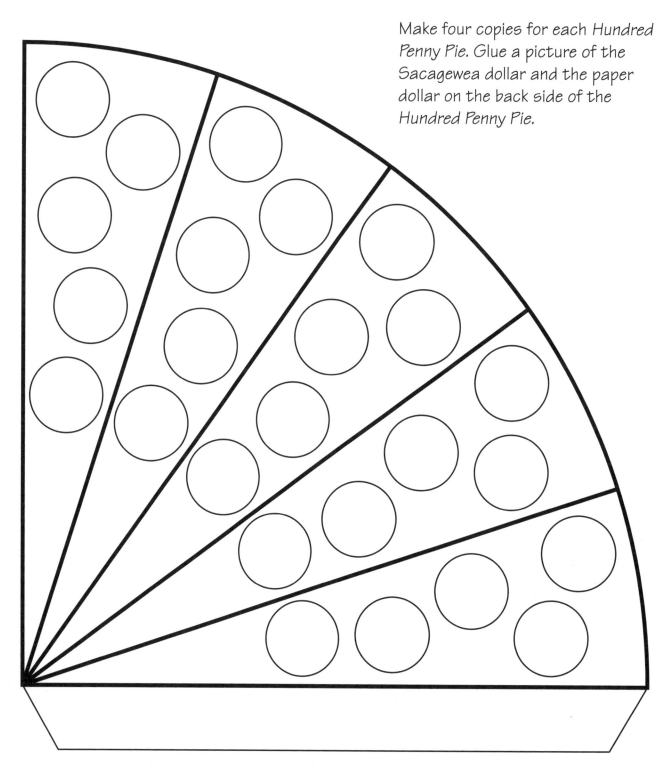

Coin Slices—five-cent slices

Hundred Penny Pie

Coin Slices—ten-cent slices

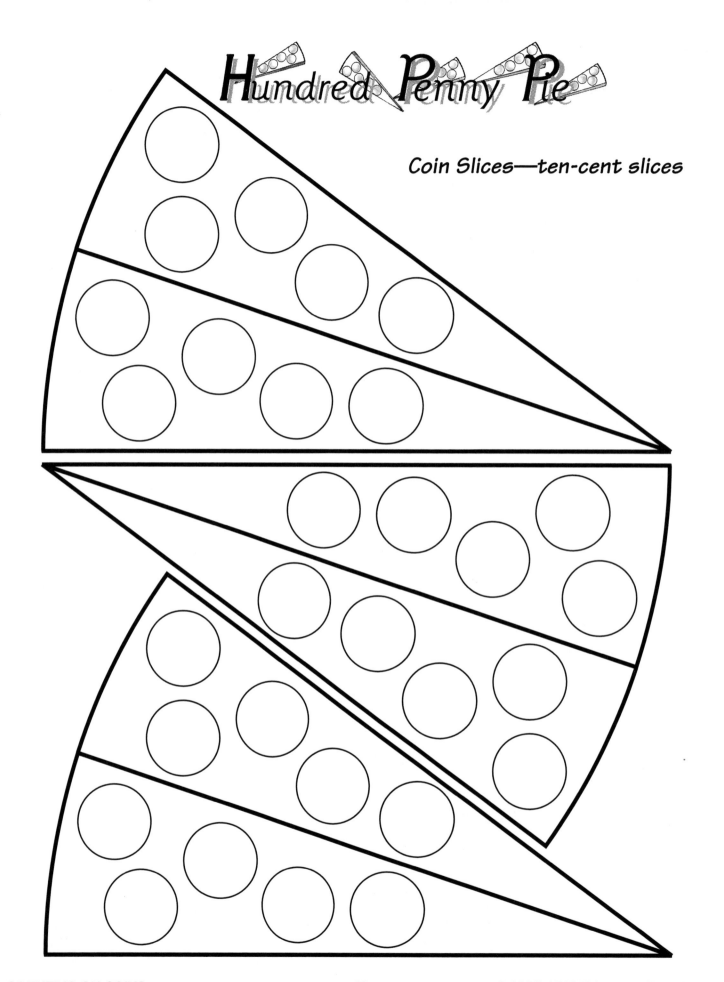

Hundred Penny Pie

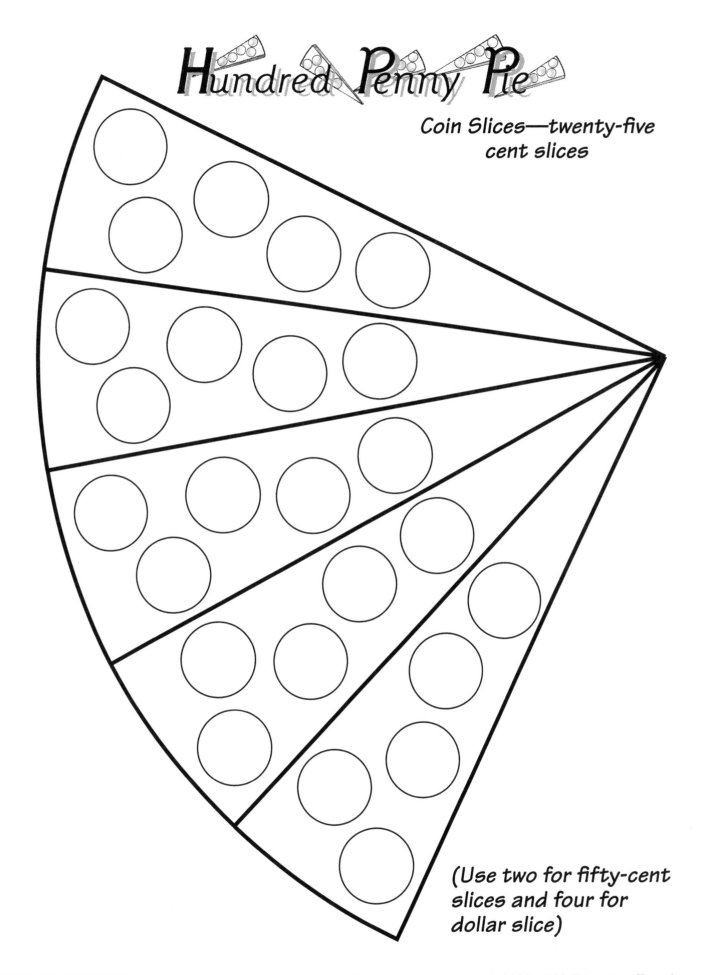

Coin Slices—twenty-five cent slices

(Use two for fifty-cent slices and four for dollar slice)

Money Pictures

Purpose of the Game
As students trade pennies for nickels, they will match real coins to their values.

Materials
For each pair of students:
  die
  gameboard, one per student
  10 pennies
  10 nickels

Management
1. Copy the gameboards onto card stock and laminate for durability.

Rules
1. One player begins by rolling the die, taking the number of pennies indicated, and placing them on the penny path. When the penny path is full, the five pennies are traded for a nickel and the nickel is put into the bank. If a player rolls a six or accumulates more than five pennies, any excess pennies are placed in the fountain until a trade is made and there are spaces available on the path.
2. The second player rolls and follows the same procedure.
3. The game is over when one player has five nickels in the bank.

Discussion
1. What kinds of coins are in your bank?
2. What kinds of coins are on the path?
3. How many pennies did you need to have before you could trade for a nickel? Why?
4. How much money is in your bank?
5. How much money is on the path?
6. Which coin is worth more, a penny or a nickel?

Extensions
1. Use the same rules to play, but trade nickels for quarters.
2. By changing the number of circles on the path and bank, the students can trade nickels for dimes, pennies for quarters.

43

Topic
Coin equivalencies

Key Question
How much money is in the treasure chest?

Learning Goal
Students will organize a large number count by trading pennies for dimes.

Guiding Document
NCTM Standards 2000*
- *Count with understanding and recognize "how many" in sets of objects*
- *Develop a sense of whole numbers and represent and use them in flexible ways, including relating, composing, and decomposing numbers*

Math
Equalities
Number sense
Skip counting
Counting on

Integrated Processes
Observing
Comparing and contrasting
Drawing conclusions

Materials
For the class:
$10 worth of pennies
$10 worth of dimes
overhead projector
treasure chest (see *Management 1*)
overhead transparency of the *Treasure Chest* grouping mat
calculator

For each student:
Treasure Chest grouping mat
tape

Background Information
Introducing students to coin trading should be done in a very concrete manner. This activity provides the tools as well as the reason for dividing a large quantity of pennies into smaller sets, combining them into manageable counting sets, and then processing them into a large number—the class total. Through this experience, students begin to develop an understanding of the efficiency and convenience of using fewer coins.

Management
1. To add interest to this activity, make or purchase a small treasure chest. This is an item that can be found in most school supply stores. Decorating a shoebox with black paper and imitation gems can provide an inexpensive treasure chest. Put the pennies into the treasure chest.
2. Make an overhead transparency of the *Treasure Chest* grouping mat.
3. The students will have to work in pairs to make the ten-penny rolls. Prior to the lesson distribute four three-inch strips of tape to each student. To make the ten-penny rolls, one student will need to place ten pennies in a stack and hold the stack between their thumb and pointer finger while their partner wraps a piece of tape around the stack so that it is no longer ten single pennies but a ten-penny roll.

Procedure
1. Tell students that you found a treasure chest full of coins. Hold up one of the pennies and ask if the students know the coin's name and its value. Have students estimate how much money they think is in the treasure chest.
2. Tell the students that everyone will help count the pennies and that you will demonstrate how the procedure will work. Ask students how many pennies they think you can hold in one hand. Grab a handful of pennies. Lay the pennies on the overhead transparency of the *Treasure Chest*. Have the students help you count the pennies aloud. When you reach ten pennies, stop and ask if anyone knows a coin that would equal ten pennies. Place the ten pennies in a stack and with the assistance of a student, create a ten-penny roll by wrapping a piece of tape around the stack so that it is no longer ten single pennies but a set of ten. Trade this ten-penny roll for one dime.

Continue counting and trading until the students have helped you organize all the pennies held in your hand. Add the dimes by skip counting by tens, add on any leftover pennies, and record this number on the coin at the bottom of the *Treasure Chest* grouping mat.

3. Tell students that the class will work together to find out how much money is in the treasure chest. Explain that each student will take one handful of pennies and place them on the *Treasure Chest* grouping mat. Ask students to organize the pennies into sets of tens. When they cannot make any more sets of ten pennies, instruct them to turn each set into a ten-penny roll and trade each roll for a dime. Have them count by tens and add on any leftover pennies to get the total number of pennies they held. Instruct them to record that total on the coin at the bottom of the mat.

4. Using a calculator, add in each child's total to determine how many coins were in the chest.

5. Discuss the efficiency of trading pennies for dimes.

Discussion

1. How many pennies did we trade for each dime? [10]

2. Why did we trade sets of ten pennies in for dimes? [One dime is equal in value to 10 cents, or 10 pennies, and it is easier to count a large number by tens than ones.]

3. How did stacking the pennies into sets of tens help you count your total number of pennies?

4. Could we have traded other sets of pennies for coins smaller than a dime? ...larger than a dime?

5. What do you notice about the number of pennies that most students could hold in their hand?

Extensions

1. Repeat the activity using nickels in the treasure chest, trading five nickels for one quarter.

2. Have students save pennies and donate them to a local charity as a service project.

* Reprinted with permission from *Principles and Standards for School Mathematics,* 2000 by the National Council of Teachers of Mathematics. All rights reserved.

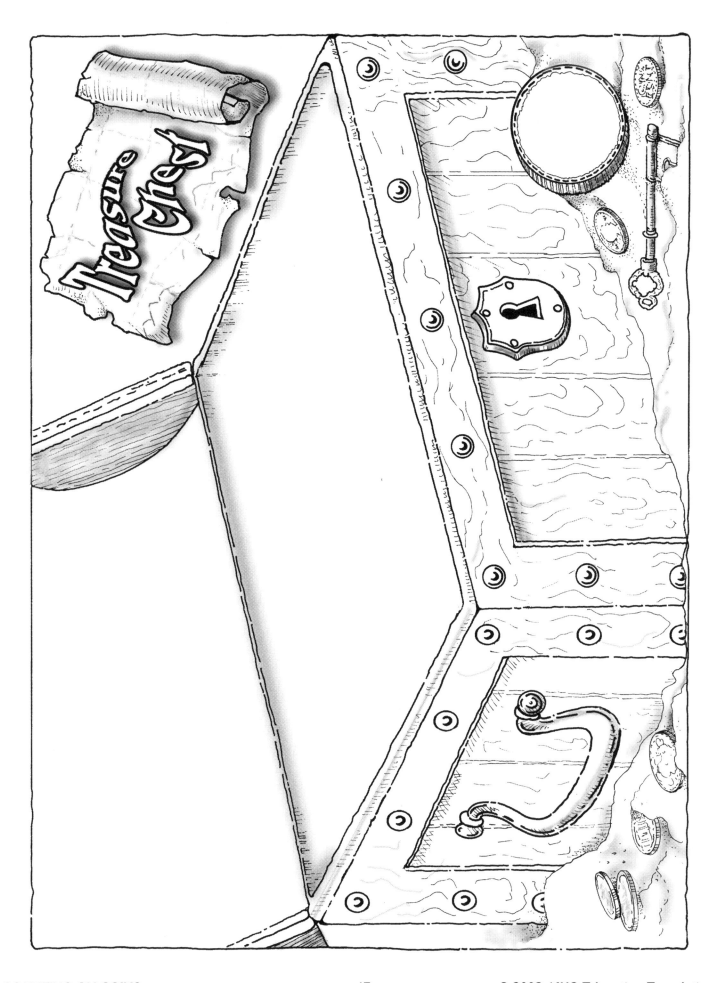

Topics
Money values
Counting

Key Question
How does skip counting and counting on help you when counting a group of coins?

Learning Goal
Students will use coins to practice counting on and skip counting.

Guiding Document
NCTM Standards 2000*
- *Count with understanding and recognize "how many" in sets of objects*
- *Develop a sense of whole numbers and represent and use them in flexible ways, including relating, composing, and decomposing numbers*

Math
Number sense
   counting on
   skip counting

Integrated Processes
Observing
Communicating
Recording data

Materials
For each group of students:
   paper bags (see *Management 1* and *2*)
   coins (see *Management 1* and *2*)

For each student:
   Money Bags recording sheet

Background Information
Specific counting skills are needed in making change, trading coins, and using money. Skills such as skip counting by fives, tens, 25s, 50s, and 100s and counting on are necessary. This lesson gives the students an opportunity to practice these skills.

Management
1. For *Part One,* prepare a paper bag of coins (money bags) for each group of four students. Place several of one type of U.S. coin in each of the bags. One bag should have only dimes, another only nickels, another only quarters, etc.
2. For *Part Two,* prepare two sets of paper bags (money bags) for each group—one containing one coin of each value (nickel, dime, quarter, etc.), and another containing only four pennies.
3. Duplicate a *Money Bags* recording sheet for each student.
4. Prior to this lesson, students need to be aware of skip counting by fives, tens, 25s, 50s, and 100s and how to count on from a number other than one.

Procedure
Part One
1. Give each group of students a bag of coins. Hand out a *Money Bags* recording sheet to each student.
2. Ask one student in each group to reach into the bag and take out three coins. Call on one group at a time to count the total of the coins using skip counting. (The group with dimes would count "ten, 20, 30 cents"; the group with nickels would count "five, ten, 15 cents"; etc.)
3. Tell students to put the coins back in the bags and pass the bags to another member in the same group. Instruct students to take out four coins and to use skip counting to count the total value of the coins. Tell them to record the kind of coin they are counting, the number of coins they took from the bag, and the total value of the coins on the *Money Bags* recording sheets.
4. Repeat this procedure until all students in the groups have had a chance to count and record. Tell them they must take a minimum of three coins and that they must take out a different number of coins each time.
5. Once the groups have completed their task, have them trade bags with another group in the class and repeat the procedure.

Part Two
1. Give each group of students two bags of coins. Tell them to use their *Money Bags* recording sheets to record their findings.
2. Direct one student in each group to take out one coin from bag one and several coins from the

penny bag. Have them count the value of the two sets of coins by starting with the coin of the greatest value. Have them count on by adding the pennies. For example, a student who draws out a quarter and three pennies would count "25, 26, 27, 28 cents." A student who draws out a dime and four pennies would count "ten, 11, 12, 13, 14 cents."

3. Using their *Money Bags* recording sheets, have students record the coins drawn and the counting on sequence used.

4. Ask students to continue with this procedure until everyone in the group has had a turn.

Discussion
1. Count by fives to 45.
2. Count by 25s to 100.
3. Starting with 25, count on by ones to 28.
4. Starting with 50, count on by ones to 54.
5. How does skip counting and counting on help you when counting money?
6. Which skip counting is easiest? ...hardest? Why?
7. When would you need to use counting on? [when counting change to pay for things]

Evidence of Learning
1. Listen for accuracy as students count the coins using skip counting and counting on methods.
2. Look for accuracy of counting the coins on the *Money Bags* recording sheets.

* Reprinted with permission from *Principles and Standards for School Mathematics*, 2000 by the National Council of Teachers of Mathematics. All rights reserved.

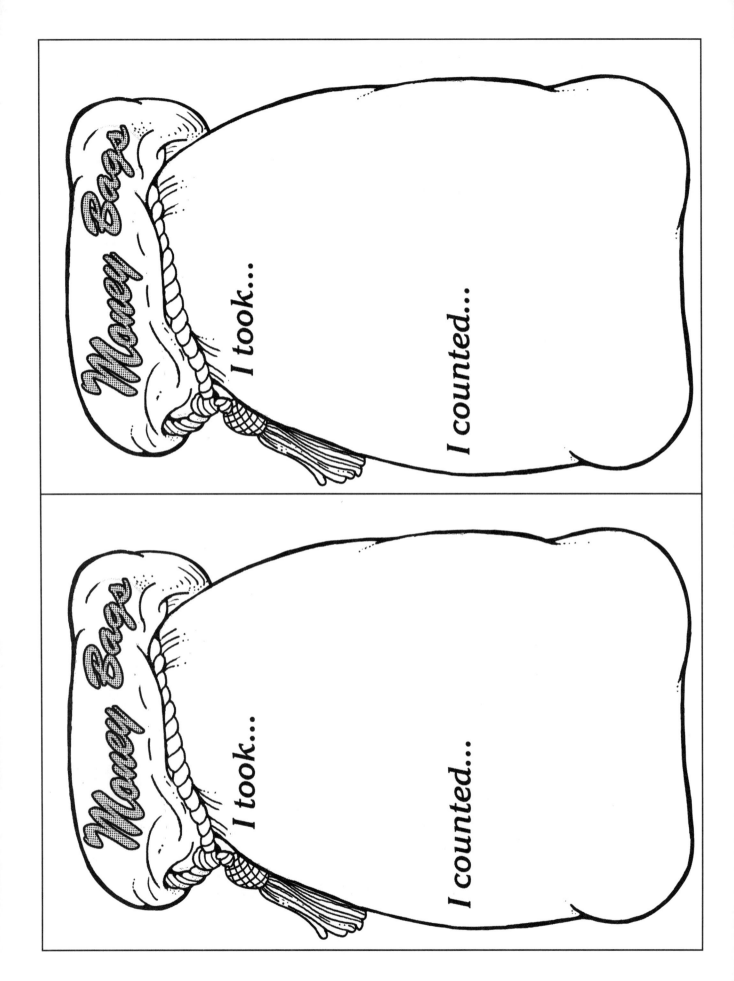

Coin Draw

Purpose of the Game
Students will play a version of tic-tac-toe by totaling the value of three coins drawn out of a sock and covering a space with that value on the gameboard.

Materials
For each pair of students:
   sock
   pennies, nickels, and dimes (see *Management 5)*
   eight marking chips, four each of two colors/types
   student sheet
   plastic cup

Management
1. This game is designed to be played in pairs. There are two versions of this game which each having the same rules but using a different gameboard and different coins.
2. Both gameboards have been placed on the same sheet of paper, but should be cut apart before being given to students to avoid confusion. Each pair of students will need one copy of the gameboard for each version.
3. All students will need four marking chips that can be visually distinguished from their partners' chips. The marking chips must be small enough to fit inside the squares on the gameboard. Math chips, Friendly Bears, different colored buttons, different kinds of beans will all work well.
4. Students will play this game by picking three coins out of a sock. The socks used should have openings large enough for students to easily fit their hands through.
5. Put a plastic cup in the toe of each sock and place the coins in the cup. The students can locate and remove the coins easily from the cup base. In *Version One* the sock must contain three pennies and three nickels. In *Version Two* the sock must contain two pennies, two nickels, and two dimes.

6. Students may eventually realize that by feeling the coins they are pulling out of the sock, they can make this less a game of chance and more a game of strategy. They should be allowed to make this discovery for themselves and not have it pointed out to them.

Rules
1. One player begins by reaching into the sock and pulling out three coins. The player must add the coins together and state their combined value out loud.
2. Any empty square with that value may be covered by the student. If there are no empty squares with that value, the student forfeits that turn, and the other player gets to draw.
3. Players take turns choosing coins and covering squares until one player has three squares in a row horizontally, vertically, or diagonally.
4. If neither player is able to get three squares in a row, the game is a draw.

© 2002 AIMS Education Foundation

3¢	11¢	7¢
15¢	3¢	11¢
3¢	15¢	7¢

Coin Draw
Version Two

11¢	20¢	7¢
12¢	7¢	12¢
21¢	16¢	25¢

Topic
Coin values

Key Question
What coins could be used to equal the values shown on the piggy banks?

Learning Goal
Students will match coins to values.

Guiding Document
NCTM Standards 2000*
- *Count with understanding and recognize "how many" in sets of objects*
- *Use a variety of methods and tools to compute, including objects, mental computation, estimation, paper and pencil, and calculators*

Math
Equalities
Number sense

Integrated Processes
Observing
Comparing and contrasting
Drawing conclusions

Materials
Set of plastic coins
Set of coin cards
Set of piggy bank cards
Pocket chart

Management
1. Copy both sets of cards onto card stock and laminate for durability. *Part One* of the activities will use only the piggy bank cards. *Part Two* will use both sets of the cards.
2. As students' skill levels increase, they can be challenged with a timed, mental math version of the matching by doing *Part Two* of this activity.
3. *Part One* of this activity is appropriate for a small group setting or can be placed in a center.

Procedure
Part One
1. Students will turn over a piggy bank card and place coins on it to equal the value shown.

2. Continue the process until all of the banks have been filled with the correct coins.

Part Two
1. Place the laminated set of piggy bank cards and coin cards in a pocket chart with the back side of the cards facing out.
2. Invite one student to the front of the room to take the 30-second challenge. Tell the student that he or she will have 30 seconds to turn the cards over and match the banks with the cards that have the same values. Use the classroom clock or a watch with a second hand to time the student's attempt. (Until students gain confidence in counting money, the time may need to be extended to 60 seconds.) This process can be repeated using different values.
3. Encourage the rest of your students to cheer on the competitor.

Discussion
1. Choose a piggy bank. What kinds of coins are in your bank?
2. How many pennies are in your banks?
3. Choose another bank. Do you have more nickels or dimes in your bank?
4. Which bank has the largest number of coins?
5. Which bank has the most money?
6. What strategy did you use to quickly match the coins and banks?

Evidence of Learning
1. Look for accuracy as students place the coins on the card to equal the values shown.
2. Look for correct matches as the students match coins and values for the 30-second challenge.

*   Reprinted with permission from *Principles and Standards for School Mathematics,* 2000 by the National Council of Teachers of Mathematics. All rights reserved.

54

Piggy Banks

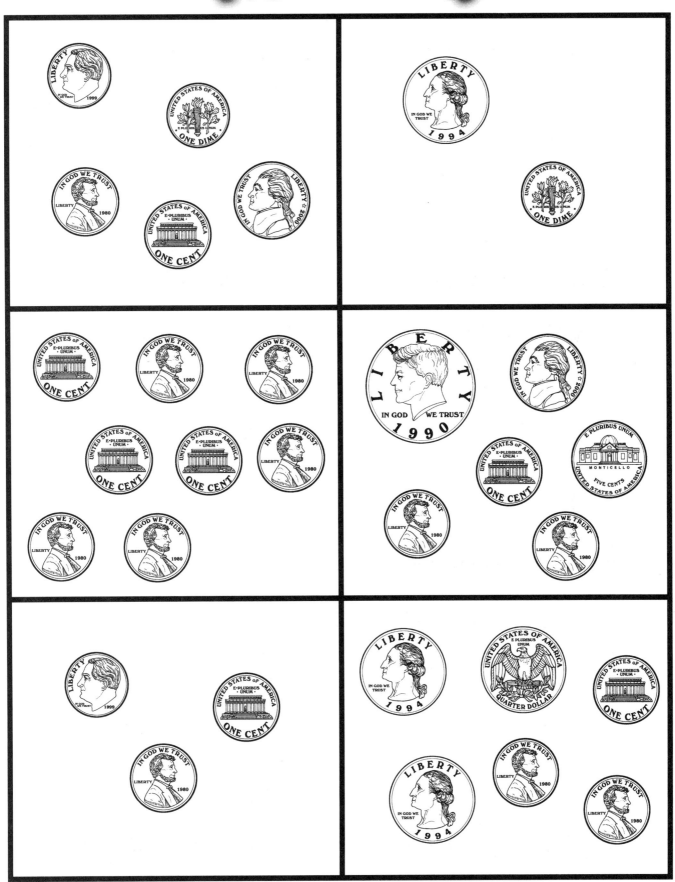

Topic
Counting Change

Key Question
How much money do you have in your pocket?

Learning Goal
Students will determine the values of various combinations of coins.

Guiding Document
NCTM Standards 2000*
- *Use a variety of methods and tools to compute, including objects, mental computation, estimation, paper and pencil, and calculators*
- *Illustrate general principles and properties of operations, such as commutativity, using specific numbers*

Math
Counting
Number and operations
    addition
    subtraction

Integrated Processes
Observing
Communicating

Materials
For each student:
    shirt handout
    glue stick
    letter-sized envelope (see *Management 1*)
    coins (see *Management 2*)

Background Information
    Counting change is often very difficult for young children. For children to be successful at counting change, they need to have multiple experiences identifying coins and their values, skip counting, counting on, and counting sets of coins. *Pockets Full-O Money* will give children an opportunity to apply many of these skills while working in a familiar context. Most children have experienced the excitement of having a few coins in their pockets and the wonder of just how much money they really have.

Management
1. Each pair of students will use one letter-sized envelope to make two pockets.
2. Prior to teaching this lesson, send home the parent letter requesting an individual set of coins for each child. The coin set should include 50 pennies, five dimes, 10 nickels, two quarters, and one half-dollar.

Procedure
1. Give each pair of students one letter-sized envelope. Have one of the students seal the envelope. Instruct them to fold the envelope in half and cut along the fold line to form two pockets.

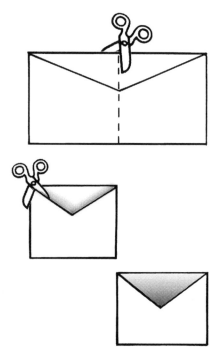

2. Tell the students to place their hand inside the opening and to cut a v-shaped section out of the top layer of the envelope. This allows more room for their hands to reach in and out of the pocket.

3. Ask students to follow the directions on the handout to create a shirt with a pocket. Tell students to glue their pockets in the designated area.

4. When the pocket construction is completed, hand out a set of coins to each child.

5. Ask the class to put $.25 into their pockets. Question students about their choice of coins. Repeatedly ask, "Is there any other possibility?" Do this until all possible combinations have been cited. Have the students record their coin combinations on the *Pockets Full-O Money* recording sheet. Young children can do a crayon rubbing to record their combination, while older children may use stamps or record the coin values symbolically.

6. Tell students to place one nickel, two pennies, and a dime into their pockets. Ask them how much money is in their pocket. Have students record the coins and the value on the recording page.

7. Ask students to empty their pockets. Walk around the room and place different combinations of coins into each student's pocket. Have students count and record the amount of money in their pockets. Ask the students to compare their amount with their neighbor's amount. Who has more?

8. Have students put four nickels into their pockets. Ask them to count out loud as they put the nickels in. [five, ten, 15, 20] Question the students about how much money they would have if they added one more nickel, two more, etc. Ask what would happen if they added a dime.

9. Tell students that you have 15 cents in your pocket. Instruct them to put coins in their pockets that would equal an amount larger than yours. Question them about their choices.

10. Continue having students place coins in their pockets to total the stated amount each time.

Discussion
1. There is $1.00 in your pocket. What kind of coins could be there?
2. You have 26 cents in your pocket. What kind of coins could be there?
3. There are four coins in your pocket that total 16 cents. What coins are in your pocket?
4. In your pocket, you have one nickel, two pennies, and a dime. How much money do you have in your pocket?
5. Where did you begin counting when you totaled the nickel, two pennies, and the dime?
6. You bought a pencil at the store. It cost 43¢. What coins could you use to pay for it?

Extensions
1. Have students put coins in their pockets. Ask them to create a riddle the rest of the class can answer describing their choice.
2. This activity can also be used as an interactive bulletin board.

Curriculum Correlation
Literature
Murphy, Stuart. *The Penny Pot.* HarperCollins. New York. 1997. (Follow along and count coins with Jessie and her friends as they are transformed into a clown, a monster, and more at the face painting booth.)

*   Reprinted with permission from *Principles and Standards for School Mathematics,* 2000 by the National Council of Teachers of Mathematics. All rights reserved.

Pockets Full-O Money

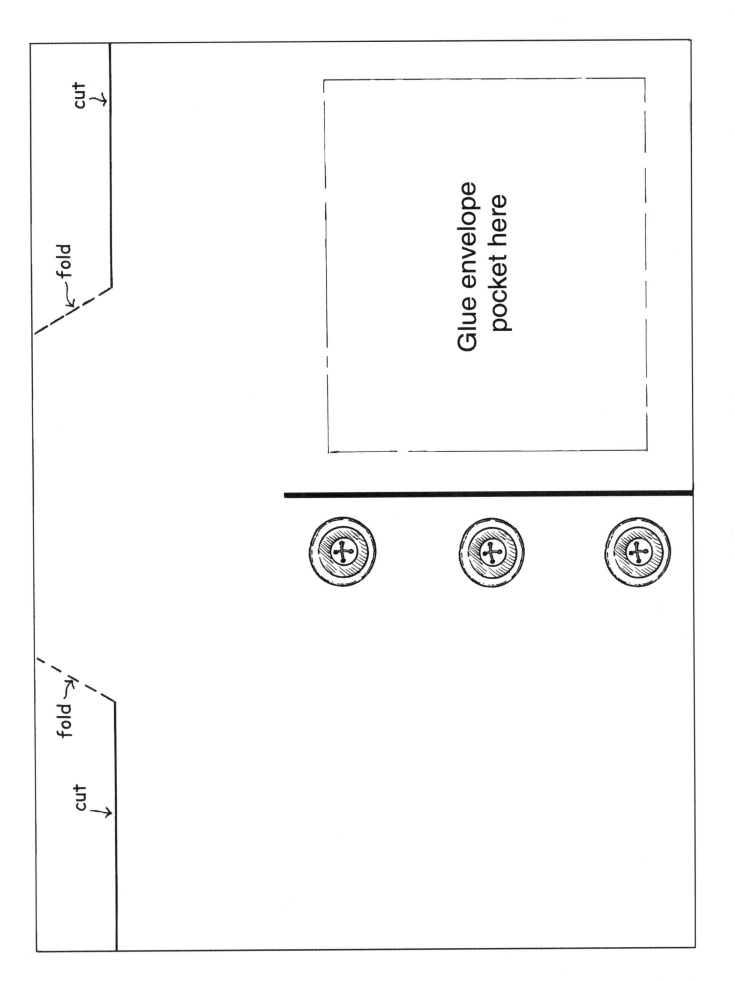

Show me the Money

Topic
Money values

Key Question
What do you have to know about coins in order to buy things with them?

Learning Goal
Students will use coins to show a variety of ways to represent specific amounts.

Guiding Document
NCTM Standards 2000*
- *Count with understanding and recognize "how many" in sets of objects*
- *Develop a sense of whole numbers and represent and use them in flexible ways, including relating, composing, and decomposing numbers*

Math
Number sense
   counting on
   skip counting

Integrated Processes
Observing
Communicating
Applying

Materials
For the class:
   one set of *Price Tags*

For each student:
   pocket chart (see *Management 1*)
   coin cards

Background Information
   The ability to apply mental math to calculate coin values and combinations will provide students with valuable life skills in using money. This lesson provides an exercise to strengthen the students' skip-counting and counting-on skills.

Management
1. For each student, prepare an individual pocket chart by following these directions.
   a. Fold an 8 " x 11" sheet of paper lengthwise as illustrated.

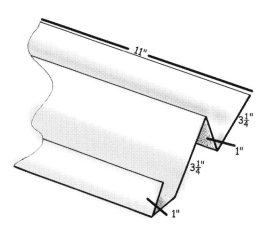

   b. Collapse the folds to form pockets and tape the edges.

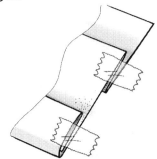

   c. Have students insert coin cards as illustrated.

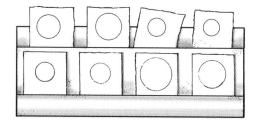

2. Duplicate several sets of coin cards for each student.
3. Duplicate and enlarge one set of *Price Tags* to use with the whole class or in a small group.

Procedure

1. Discuss how it is important to be able to use coins quickly when making a purchase in a store. Remind students that when people carry coins, the combinations in their purses or pockets can change each time they make a purchase. They can either receive coins or give away coins in the process of the purchase.

2. Inform students that they must exchange only a portion of their money and that they cannot simply exchange the complete collection. Explain that if they are asked to pay 35 cents for an item, the types of coins they have in their pockets or purses will determine the combination of coins they can use to pay this amount. For example, if an item is 35 cents, and the students do not have any quarters, they may need to use three dimes and a nickel to pay for the item. On the other hand, if the students do not have any dimes, they may use one quarter and two nickels to pay for the item. Discuss other combinations the students could use to purchase a 35-cent item.

3. Give each student a pocket chart and several sets of coin cards. Have them cut the cards apart. Show the students a price tag and ask them to arrange a combination of coin cards in the pocket chart to represent coins they could use to purchase the item pictured.

4. Have students share their cards with the class and discuss all the different combinations that could be used to purchase the item on the *Price Tag*.

5. Continue this process, showing a different *Price Tag* each time.

Extensions

1. Have the students record the different combinations for each item. Organize and display the different combinations for each specific price tag.

2. Instead of using the price tags provided with this lesson, use pictures and prices of items from a catalog or advertisement. Use restaurant menus or other real-world prices that might be of interest to your students.

Evidence of Learning

1. Listen for accuracy as students describe possible combinations of coins for purchasing specifically priced items.

2. Look for accuracy in the arrangement of coin cards in the student pocket charts.

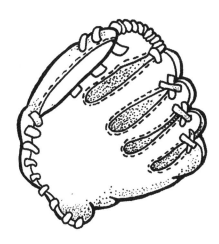

Discussion

1. Which coins did you use most often in your combinations? ...least?

2. What coins could you use to pay for an item that costs 56 cents?

3. Describe two different ways to pay for an item that costs 25 cents.

4. Why is it important to know different ways to combine coins to equal the same value?

Show Me the Money

Show Me the Money

Show Me the Money—Coin Cards

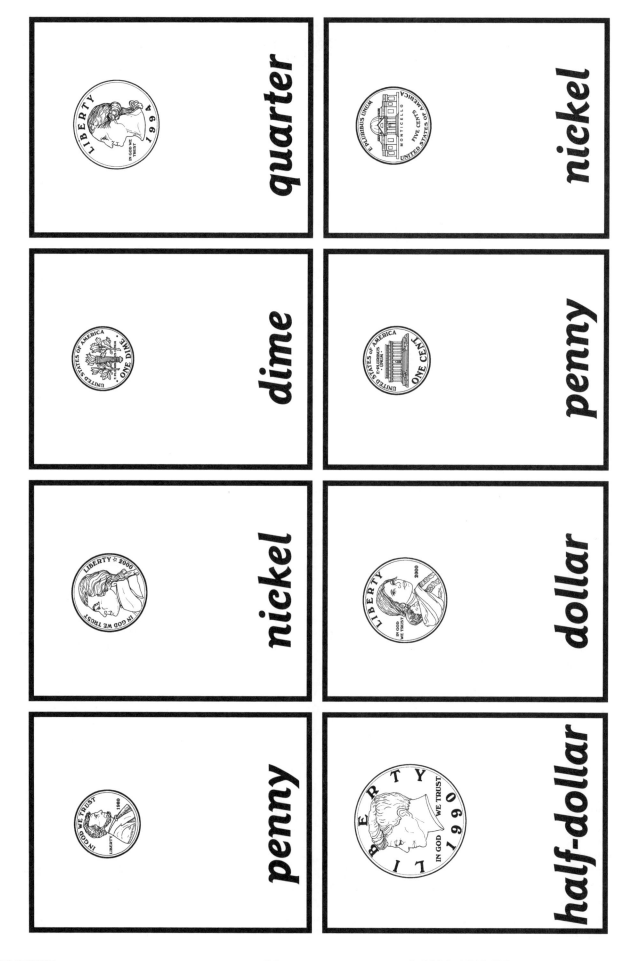

quarter

nickel

dime

penny

nickel

dollar

penny

half-dollar

Making Cents of Dollars

Topics
Money values
Making change

Learning Goals
Students will:
1. exchange coins to equal specific values, and
2. count to find the total of a combination of coins.

Guiding Document
NCTM Standards 2000*
- *Count with understanding and recognize "how many" in sets of objects*
- *Develop a sense of whole numbers and represent and use them in flexible ways, including relating, composing, and decomposing numbers*
- *Build new mathematical knowledge through problem solving*
- *Solve problems that arise in mathematics and in other contexts*

Math
Number sense
    counting on
    skip counting
    equivalencies

Integrated Processes
Observing
Comparing and contrasting
Communicating

Materials
For each student:
    various coins (see *Management 1*)
    recloseable plastic bag
    AIMS Buck
    sheet of paper coins
    scissors
    glue

For the class:
    bell

Background Information
Young learners quite often enter school knowing the names of coins. This does not indicate an understanding of the value of money. This lesson provides practice in exchanging one type of coin for another. The students begin to construct an understanding of coin equivalencies and coin values. When teaching the value of money, number sense is developed through counting, trading, addition, and subtraction.

Management
1. For each student, prepare a collection of coins that equals one dollar and place them in a recloseable plastic bag. Include different combinations of coins for each student. For example, one student may have 100 pennies; another may have 20 nickels; another may have three quarters, two dimes and one nickel; etc.
2. Duplicate several *AIMS Bucks* for the students to use as recording sheets.
3. Duplicate at least one sheet of paper coins for each student.

Procedure
1. Give each student a collection of coins. Ask students to count out their coins to find the total in their collection. [$1.00] Explain that when the bell is rung, they are to find a partner. Ring the bell and wait for partners to be formed.
2. Direct the partners to exchange equivalent values of money. Inform students that they must exchange only a portion of their money and that they cannot simply exchange the complete collection. For example, if one partner has five nickels and the other partner has a quarter, they may exchange the nickels for a quarter.
3. Explain that the object of this game is to make several exchanges with different partners and still have the total of one dollar at the end of the game. Tell them that they do not know when the game will end, so they must be careful to make accurate exchanges each time.
4. Ring the bell again and direct students to find new partners and make their exchanges.
5. Continue this procedure through several exchanges and call the game when it seems appropriate to stop by saying, "It's dollar time!" Have the students count their coins to find the total. If they have a dollar, they were successful in their exchanges. If they have more or less than a dollar, there was a mistake along the way. If one student has a total other than a dollar, there will be at least one other student, if not more, with a total other than a dollar.
6. Give an *AIMS Buck* to each student whose total at the end of the game equaled a dollar. Hand out a sheet of paper coins, scissors, and glue to each student. Ask them to cut and paste a record of the coins on their *AIMS Buck* to indicate their combination of coins that equaled a dollar.
7. If there are students who do not have a dollar left in their hand, redistribute the money between

those students and have them play the exchange game again. Once they reach the end of the game with a coin collection that equals a dollar, have them record their combinations using the *AIMS Bucks*. An alternative is to have these students use their coins to make a dollar in change for each student involved. Once they each have coins that equal a dollar, give them *AIMS Bucks* to record their combinations.

8. Display the different *AIMS Bucks* to show the many different combinations students found that equal one dollar.

9. Discuss the different exchanges students made throughout the game.

10. Challenge students to find additional combinations of coins to equal a dollar that were not shown in the class display. Provide additional *AIMS Bucks* for recording and displaying any new combinations.

Discussion

1. Describe some of the exchanges you made throughout the game.

2. How many dimes and nickels might you get in exchange for a quarter? [one dime and three nickels, two dimes and one nickel, or five nickels]

3. What combination used the fewest number of coins to equal a dollar? [two half-dollors] Describe another possible combination that would use just a few coins to equal a dollar. [four quarters]

4. Name the combination of coins equaling a dollar that uses the most coins. [100 pennies]

5. Describe how you counted your coins to find the total.

6. Was there a time when you could not make an exchange? Why?

Extensions

1. Instead of exchanging to equal a dollar, have the class exchange to equal 75 cents, 35 cents, or other target totals.

2. Play the game as a relay. Divide the class into two or more relay teams. Give each relay team a total of one dollar in change in a plastic bag. At a designated distance away from each team, place a collection of change in a bowl. At the start of the race the first person in each line is to run to the bowls, make an exchange of money, and race back with their coins, handing the bag of coins to the next person in line. This person runs to the bowls, makes another exchange, and races back to the line. This continues until all members of the relay teams have had a chance to make a coin exchange. Once the teams have completed their exchanges, they must count their coins. If they have a total of one dollar, they are finished.

If they do not, they lose the relay. The team that completes all exchanges and ends up with a dollar in their bag first, is declared the winner.

Evidence of Learning

1. Look for correct exchanges of coins while students play the game.

2. Listen for accuracy as students describe their coin combinations.

3. Listen for accuracy as students count their coins to find a total of their combinations.

Curriculum Correlation

Literature

Adams, Barbara Johnston. *The Go-Around Dollar.* Four Winds Press. New York. 1992. (A story describing how a single dollar changes hands, accompanied by facts about the one-dollar bill.)

Hoban, Lillian. *Arthur's Funny Money.* Harper & Row. New York. 1981. (When Violet has a numbers problem and Arthur is penniless, they go into business and solve both problems.)

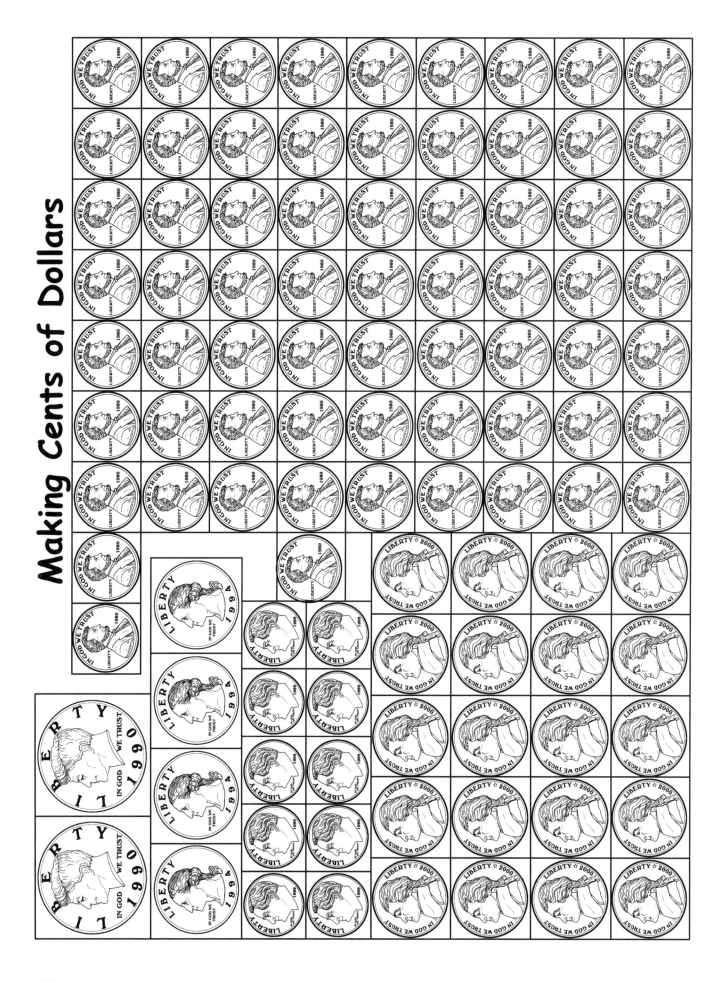

Making Cents of Dollars

Who's $mart?

Topic
Money values, making change

Key Question
How does the poem *Smart* by Shel Silverstein help us better understand coins?

Learning Goals
Students will:
1. make the coin amounts given in the poem with play money, and
2. compare the value of the combination of coins with the amount of coins involved in each trade.

Guiding Document
NCTM Standards 2000*
- *Count with understanding and recognize "how many" in sets of objects*
- *Connect number words and numerals to the quantities they represent, using various physical models and representations*
- *Understand various meanings of addition and subtraction of whole numbers and the relationship between the two operations*
- *Understand the effects of adding and subtracting whole numbers*

Math
Whole number operations
    addition
    subtraction

Integrated Processes
Observing
Recording
Comparing and contrasting
Communicating
Applying

Materials
Play money (see *Management 2*)
Smart by Shel Silverstein (see *Management 3*)
Chart paper
Lined paper
Student book

Background Information
Often children learn the names of coins without any understanding of their values. The boy in the poem *Smart* by Shel Silverstein is a perfect example of someone with a good understanding of number values and no understanding of coin values. This activity provides an opportunity for students to compare the number of coins to their total value. Through this experience children will build a better understanding of coin equivalencies and coin values.

Management
1. Students may need some assistance in constructing the student book.
2. Each student will need a collection of play money that should include one dollar bill, two quarters, three dimes, four nickels, and five pennies. If play money is not available, copies of the coin pictures included in *Making Cents of Dollars* can be used.
3. A copy of the poem should be available for the students to read along as you reread it. This poem can be found in the book *Where the Sidewalk Ends* by Shel Silverstein (HarperCollins. New York. 1974.).

Procedure
1. Read the poem *Smart* by Shel Silverstein to the class. Encourage a discussion of the poem.
2. Ask students if they feel the boy in the poem made good trades. Invite students to respond to the question in writing on lined paper. Have the students share their thinking with the class. Record their thoughts on chart paper.
3. Give each student a collection of play money and a copy of the student book. Ask them to identify the dollar bill. Explain that they will be rereading the poem with you and after each stanza they will determine the amount of money the boy in the poem has.
4. Read the first stanza together. After reading the stanza, instruct the students to act out the swap described in the poem and compare the amounts. Discuss the results and record the transaction on chart paper.
5. Continue reading each additional stanza, acting out each exchange, comparing the amounts, discussing, and recording the amount lost each time

until the poem is completed. End the lesson by discussing whether students think the boy's father was really too proud to speak.

Discussion

1. Describe some of the trading that took place in the poem.
2. What do you think about the boy's knowledge of money?
3. Do you think that the boy's father in the poem was really proud of him? Explain your answer.
4. How much money did the boy lose after all of the trading was completed?
5. What should you do if someone offers to trade money with you?

6. Did the boy in the poem learn a valuable lesson about money? Why or why not?

Evidence of Learning

1. Look for accuracy as the students make the coin amounts given in the poem and act out the money exchanges.
2. Listen for logical explanations of why the boy in the poem did not make good deals as the students compare the values of the combinations of coins with the number of coins involved in each trade.

* Reprinted with permission from *Principles and Standards for School Mathematics*, 2000 by the National Council of Teachers of Mathematics. All rights reserved.

Who's $mart?

Booklet

Cut the pages along the broken lines. Extend the left side of the book to the edge of the paper to allow room for stapling. Place the pages in order starting with the smallest tab on the first page and ending with the full page on the back.

$MART

name _____

$MART

name _____

★☆★☆★☆★☆★☆★☆★☆★☆★☆★☆★☆★☆

I had _____. I swapped it for _____.

Was that a good swap? _____, because

_____

_____.

☆★☆★☆★☆★☆★☆★☆★☆★☆★☆★☆★☆★

★☆★☆★☆★☆★☆★☆★☆★☆★☆★☆★☆★☆

I had _____. I swapped it for _____.

Was that a good swap? _____, because

_____

_____.

☆★☆★☆★☆★☆★☆★☆★☆★☆★☆★☆★☆★

☆☆☆☆☆☆☆☆☆☆☆☆☆☆☆☆☆☆☆☆☆☆

I had _____. I swapped it for _____.

Was that a good swap? _____, because

_____

_____.

☆☆☆☆☆☆☆☆☆☆☆☆☆☆☆☆☆☆☆☆☆☆

☆☆☆☆☆☆☆☆☆☆☆☆☆☆☆☆☆☆☆☆☆☆

I had _____. I swapped it for _____.

Was that a good swap? _____, because

_____

_____.

☆☆☆☆☆☆☆☆☆☆☆☆☆☆☆☆☆☆☆☆☆☆

☆☆☆☆☆☆☆☆☆☆☆☆☆☆☆☆☆☆☆☆☆☆

I had ___$1.00___. I swapped it for _____.

Was that a good swap? _____, because

_____

_____.

☆☆☆☆☆☆☆☆☆☆☆☆☆☆☆☆☆☆☆☆☆☆

☆☆☆☆☆☆☆☆☆☆☆☆☆☆☆☆☆☆☆☆☆☆

Was his dad really proud of him? _____,

because_____

_____

_____.

☆☆☆☆☆☆☆☆☆☆☆☆☆☆☆☆☆☆☆☆☆☆

Alexander's Not Rich Anymore

Topic
Money values, counting coins

Key Question
How do we use money in real-world situations?

Learning Goals
The students will:
1. identify each coin and its value,
2. count various coin values up to totals of one dollar,
3. spend money and keep track of how much money is being spent, and
4. use calculators to add and subtract coins with like and unlike monetary values.

Guiding Document
NCTM Standards 2000*
- *Count with understanding and recognize "how many" in sets of objects*
- *Connect number words and numerals to the quantities they represent, using various physical models and representations*
- *Understand various meanings of addition and subtraction of whole numbers and the relationship between the two operations*
- *Understand the effects of adding and subtracting whole numbers*

Math
Whole number operations
    addition
    subtraction

Integrated Processes
Observing
Recording
Comparing and contrasting
Communicating
Applying

Materials
Alexander, Who Used to be Rich Last Sunday by Judith Viorst
Play money (see *Management 1*)
Chalkboard or chart paper (see *Management 2*)
Calculators, one per two students
Various store items (see *Management 4*)

Shopping list
Student recording pages

Background Information
Children must first have multiple experiences in which they identify coins, assign value to coins, and count collections of coins. To further students' understanding of money and how our monetary system works, it is then necessary to expose them to real-world applications.

During this lesson, the students will be engaging in real-world situations in which they will be required to add and subtract using play money and calculators.

Management
1. Each pair of students will need a collection of play money that should include two one-dollar bills, four quarters, five dimes, seven nickels, and eighteen pennies.
2. The list mentioned in *Part Two* of this activity should be made on the chalkboard or on chart paper so that it remains in the students' view.
3. Students will work in partners for *Part One* and *Part Two* of the lesson and individually for *Part Three*.
4. Several items that would interest your students will need to be clearly marked with price tags that do not exceed 50 cents and displayed around the classroom prior to teaching *Part Three* of this activity. Possible items may include erasers, small promotional items from fast food restaurants, etc.
5. Each group will need three copies of the student recording page for *Part Two*. Cut calculator pages in half and tape together to make strips of nine calculators. Each student pair will need two of these strips, one for each character.

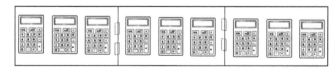

6. Each student will need one copy of the shopping list page for *Part Three* of this lesson.

Procedure
Part One
1. Read the book *Alexander, Who Used to be Rich Last Sunday* by Judith Viorst aloud to the class.

2. After reading the story, assign each student a partner. Distribute one calculator and one set of play money to each pair of students.

3. Explain to the students that they will be using the calculator and play money to keep track of Alexander's money transactions as you reread the story. Tell them that they will use their play money to first count out the amounts and then check their answers using the calculators.

4. Reread the story through the part where Alexander's grandparents give him a dollar. Have each group remove a one-dollar bill from their set of play money. Explain that one dollar is represented as 1.00 on a calculator. Instruct the students to key 1.00 into their calculators to represent Alexander's dollar.

5. Continue reading until you read about Alexander spending 15 cents on gum. Ask your students whether they should add 15 cents to their dollar or subtract 15 cents from their dollar. Ask the students how they can take 15 cents from their dollar. Guide them to discover that they will have to trade the dollar in for three quarters, two dimes, and one nickel. Instruct them to make the trade, and then take 15 cents from the change.

6. After physically manipulating the play money, lead your students through the calculator record of the transaction by instructing them to key in the subtraction sign and 15 cents (.15).

7. Continue reading until Alexander's dad fines him a dime for saying bad things to his brothers. Instruct your students to subtract the dime first from their play money and then on the calculator.

8. Continue the process of reading and subtracting money, trading coins when necessary, until Alexander no longer has any money and students have no more of their dollar left.

9. Talk about all the ways Alexander used his money. Ask the students if they feel that Alexander used his money wisely.

Part Two
1. Ask the class which of Alexander's brothers had the most money. Encourage them to generate ways that they could find out which brother had the most money. Allow them to make a prediction. Record their predictions on the chalkboard or chart paper.

2. Distribute one set of coins, a calculator, and a long calculator strip to each pair of students.

3. Reread the first page of *Alexander, Who Used to be Rich Last Sunday* to the class. As you read about the coins and bills Anthony had, list them on the chalkboard or chart paper.

4. Ask each pair to gather two one-dollar bills, three quarters, one dime, seven nickels, and eighteen pennies from their set of coins.

5. Remind the class of their work with the calculators in *Part One* of this activity. Explain that they will

be using the calculators to determine how much money Anthony had. Ask if anyone recalls how to represent one dollar on a calculator. Discuss what it would look like. [1.00] Have a student instruct the class in the correct way to represent two dollars on a calculator. Invite each group to key 2.00 into their calculators.

6. Bring the students' attention to the calculator strips. Tell them that they will be recording on a paper calculator what they are doing on the real calculators. First tell them to write their names at the top of the strip. Then have them write *Anthony* because they will determine how much money he had. Instruct them to record 2.00 in the correct place on the recording sheet so that their paper calculators look like their real calculators. Have them shade in the plus sign on the paper calculator.

7. Refer back to the list of Anthony's money. Ask the class how many quarters Anthony had. Count together by 25s: 25, 50, 75. Ask if anyone knows how 75 cents would be entered into a calculator. If no one offers the correct answer, direct the students to push the plus sign since they will be adding the 75 cents to the two dollars and to then key .75 into the calculator and press the equal sign. Remind them to record the .75 in the top window of the second paper calculator and shade in the equal sign. Direct them to record the new total on the third paper calculator. Continue this process until they have reached the total amount of money that Anthony had.

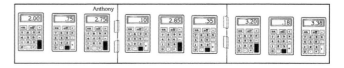

8. Hand out the second paper strip. Repeat the procedure to find out how much money Nicholas had. Compare the two amounts and determine which brother had the most money. Compare the actual results to the class predictions.

9. Discuss other combinations of coins and bills that Anthony and Nicholas could have had and still had the same amount of money.

Part Three
1. Display several items that would be of interest to your students around the classroom. Be sure that all items are clearly marked with price tags.

2. Question the students about ways to spend a dollar. Ask them what they would buy if they had a dollar.

3. Draw the students' attentions to the items displayed around the classroom. Tell them that they are going to pretend that they have one dollar to spend. Inform them that they are to walk around

the room and make a list of items that they wish to purchase, keeping in mind that they have only one dollar to spend.

4. Give each student a copy of the shopping list page. Assist the students in folding their papers into thirds. As the students shop, have them write the name or draw a picture of each item they choose to buy in the first column of their papers. Instruct them to write the amounts on the price tags in the second columns of their shopping lists. When they have made their final decisions, ask them to return to their seats. Make certain that they understand that they have one dollar to spend, they do not have to spend exactly one dollar; however, they cannot spend more than one dollar.

5. Have each student look at the first item he or she wants to purchase. Using the play money, ask students to find the correct coins to make that purchase. Tell them to make a rubbing of the coins in the third column across from the first amount as a recording. Instruct the students to repeat this process for each item that they wish to purchase.

6. When the students have completed their lists, have them find the total cost for their lists. (You may choose to let them use calculators.)

7. Allow the students to share their shopping lists with the class. Have the class calculate the total amount of money spent by each student. Discuss with the class what coins and bills might be used to pay for each student's list of items.

Discussion
1. What do you know about money?
2. How are coins alike? How are they different?
3. Which of Alexander's brothers—Anthony or Nicholas—had the most money? Explain your answer.
4. Why do we need money?

5. Why is it important to be able to count money?
6. How do we use money?
7. If you had $1.00 to spend, how would you spend it?
8. How did Alexander get his money?
9. In the end, was Alexander happy with the way he used his money? Explain.
10. What have you spent money for and later wished you had not spent it? How did it make you feel?
11. Do you ever save money? What kinds of things do you save for?
12. Why did Alexander end up with only bus tokens?

Extensions
1. Have the students write and publish their own sequels to this story. They may choose to write about what would happen if Alexander's grandparents gave him another dollar or if he found money on the playground.
2. Let students create a class store. Using play money, allow them to sell items to other classes.

Evidence of Learning
1. Listen for accuracy as students identify each coin and its value.
2. Observe students matching coins to given money amounts.
3. Listen for accuracy as students add and subtract money with different coins up to and down from one dollar.

Curriculum Correlation
Viorst, Judith. *Alexander, Who Used to Be Rich Last Sunday.* Scholastic, Inc. New York. 1978. (Although Alexander and his money are quickly parted, he comes to realize all the things that can be done with a dollar.)

* Reprinted with permission from *Principles and Standards for School Mathematics,* 2000 by the National Council of Teachers of Mathematics. All rights reserved.

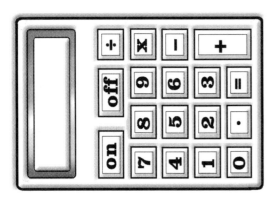
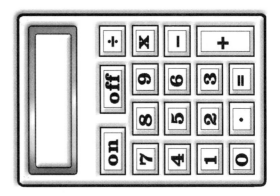
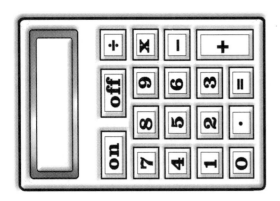
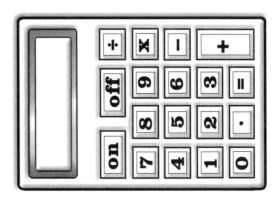
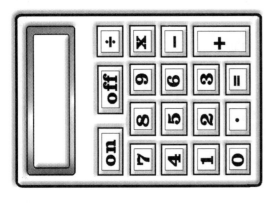
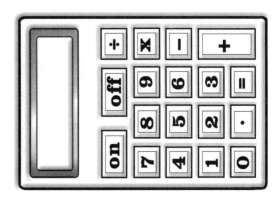

78

Rubbing	Cost	Item
	Total Cost _____	

Topic
Money

Key Question
Why is it important to be able to add and subtract money?

Learning Goals
Students will:
1. identify coins needed to buy items priced at $5.00 or less, and
2. solve problems using money by estimating costs and making change.

Guiding Document
NCTM Standards 2000*
- *Count with understanding and recognize "how many" in sets of objects*
- *Connect number words and numerals to the quantities they represent, using various physical models and representations*
- *Understand various meanings of addition and subtraction of whole numbers and the relationship between the two operations*
- *Understand the effects of adding and subtracting whole numbers*

Math
Whole number operations
    addition
    subtraction

Integrated Processes
Observing
Recording
Comparing and contrasting
Communicating
Applying

Materials
Student book club order form (see *Management 1*)
Play money (see *Management 2*)
Overhead transparency (see *Management 4*)

Background Information
Often children can tell you the names of coins, identify their values, and even count a collection of coins.

However, this does not necessarily mean that they are able to make the connection between these classroom skills and the use of money in real-world situations. Although it is important to teach the skills, ultimately we want our students to be able use money successfully in the real world. This activity will allow students to practice these classroom skills and apply them to a real-world situation—buying books through a school book club.

Management
1. For this activity, use the current student book club order form or make copies of the book club form included in this lesson by copying the front to the back and folding the page in half.
2. Each student will need a collection of play money that should include five one-dollar bills, four quarters, five dimes, five nickels, and ten pennies. If play money is not available, copies of the coin pictures included in this lesson can be used.
3. Make sure students realize that they are not actually ordering books in *Part Two* of this activity; remind them that it is a simulation.
4. Make an overhead transparency of the book club order form.

Procedure
Part One
1. Distribute one book club order form and collection of play money to each student. Assist the students in making the order forms into booklets.
2. Discuss where the book number, title, and price for each book are located.
3. Ask students to remove five dimes from their collection of coins. Have them count by tens to determine the total value.
4. Instruct the students to look through the order form and identify any books they could purchase with 50 cents. Discuss why they could buy some books and not buy others. [They do not have enough money to buy some books, etc.]
5. Select a book price, such as 95 cents, and ask the students to identify which coins would be needed to buy a book that costs that much. Discuss the many possible answers. Count the suggested collections of coins to see if they total 95 cents.
6. Encourage the students to identify the books they could buy with that amount of money.

7. Ask the students how much more money they would need to add to that amount if they wanted to buy a book that costs $1.95, $1.75, etc.
8. Repeat procedures five through seven using different book prices up to $5.00.

Part Two
1. The students will use the book club order forms previously used in *Part One* of this activity.
2. Review the location of the book number, title, and price for each book.
3. Select a book title from the order form that costs 95 cents. Ask the students if they could buy the book with 50 cents. Discuss how they would have to have *about* one dollar to purchase the book. By counting on from 95 cents, help the students determine how much change they would get back if they paid for the book with $1.00. [96, 97, 98, 99, $1.00] This could be counted using pennies, which could be exchanged for one nickel.
4. Draw the students' attention to a book title that costs $1.95.
5. Ask them, "About how much money would you have to have to buy this book?" The students may need some prompting with questions such as, "Would you need *about* one dollar? Why or why not? Would you need *about* two dollars?"
6. When the students have determined *about* how much money they will need, assist them in counting on from $1.95 to $2.00 to determine how much change they will get back if they pay for the book with $2.00. Repeat this process until the students are confident with estimating costs and making change.

Part Three
1. When the students are able to estimate costs and make change, bring their attention to the order section of the book club form.
2. Ask the students what they should do if they would like to buy more than one book. Demonstrate how to add the price of two books by lining up the decimal points.
3. Select two books from the order form and ask the students to find the total cost. Check their work. Allow the students to have several opportunities to practice adding two or more book prices.
4. When the students are able to add the prices of two or more books, bring their attention to the order section of the book club form.
5. Tell the students that they are going to practice ordering books. Tell them that they will have $5.00 of play money with which to order books. You may choose to have them purchase as many books as possible with their money, or you may allow them to make that decision on their own.
6. Encourage the students to first list their book choices and prices on scratch paper. This will allow them to easily add them and make changes

if their total values exceed $5.00. When they have selected their books, added their prices, and determined that the total value of their order is less than $5.00, instruct them to record the book numbers, titles, and amounts on the order form at the back of their book club form.
7. Allow the students to share their choices, and as they do, record their information on the overhead transparency of the order form. Discuss about how much each book costs and what change they will get back from their $5.00.

Discussion
1. Which books could you buy if you had 50 cents?
2. Which coins could be used to pay for a book that costs $.95?
3. If you had $5.00, which book(s) could you buy? How much change would you get back?
4. If you buy a book that costs 95 cents and pay for it with a one-dollar bill, will you get any change back? How much?
5. Why is it important to be able to count, add, and subtract money?

Extensions
1. Tell students that they have a certain amount of spending money and allow them to "shop" in catalogs, sale ads, etc.
2. Give students a sale ad and a list of items to purchase (possibly school supplies), and ask them to determine how much it will cost to purchase all of the items on the list.

Evidence of Learning
1. Check for accuracy as the students identify coin combinations that total specific book values.
2. Listen for accuracy as students determine *about* how much money they will need to purchase specific books, and as they count on, to determine how much change they will get back.

* Reprinted with permission from *Principles and Standards for School Mathematics,* 2000 by the National Council of Teachers of Mathematics. All rights reserved.

6. Measuring Max
by Alma Foote
$1.95

5. Jaguar Journal
by Drew Spotter
$2.50

7. It's About Time
by Ima Late
$1.75

8. Soccer Sam
by John Kick
$1.00

9. All About Insects
by James Cricket
with Realistic Ant
$2.75

Club
AIMS Book

2. Dinomite Riddles
by T. Rex Saurus
.75¢

3. Shellarella
by Shelly Fisher
.50¢

4. Rocket Racers
by Wendy Driver
Free Racer Replica
.95¢

1. Cat Tales
by Tabitha Catnip
.95¢

Book Order Form

name _____

Number	Title	Amount
		.
		.
		.
		.
		.
		.

Total Amount

LAST CHANCE TO ORDER

NEW

Counting Cats

10. Counting Cats
by Tom Feline

$1.50

Apples are Red

11. Apples are Red
by Rouge Caramel

$3.50

SILLY SNAKES

12. Silly Snakes
by Chuck Serpentine

$2.00

HOW TO DRAW DOGS

13. How to Draw Pack
by Chi Chow

$4.50

with Markers

Shopping Spree

Purpose of the Game
Students will play a version of tic-tac-toe by choosing different items to purchase that total the sum they want to cover on the gameboard.

Materials
Marking chips in two colors/types
Crayons or colored pencils
Dimes, nickels, and pennies *(Pet Shop)*
Student gameboard(s)

Management
1. There are two different versions of this game, which are identical in concept, but differ in their level of difficulty. In *Pet Shop*, students must buy two or more animals, total the cost, and cover that space with a marking chip. In *School Shopping*, students must buy two items, total the cost, and cover that space with a marking chip.
2. The games are designed to be played in pairs. Each pair of students will need one copy of the student gameboard for every round that they play.
3. For both games, each student will need four marking chips that can be easily distinguished from their partner's chips. The marking chips must be small enough to fit inside the squares on the gameboard. Math chips, Friendly Bears, different colored buttons, different kinds of beans, etc., will all work well.
4. For *Pet Shop*, each pair of students will need several pennies, nickels, and dimes.
5. Because *Pet Shop* involves addition and/or multiplication of several numbers, there is an additional student sheet provided to help students calculate the value of the animals they choose. On this sheet there are four pictures of each animal. These pictures are to be covered with coins corresponding to the value of the animal. For example, if a student wishes to buy two kittens and two goldfish, he or she would use a penny to cover each goldfish that is being purchased, and a nickel to cover each kitten that is being purchased. The coins can then be totaled to determine the value of the purchase, and a marking chip can be placed on a square with that value. This sheet can be shared by both students, since the coins are removed after each turn.

Rules
Pet Shop (Concrete)
1. One player begins by choosing two or more animals to purchase. Those animals are covered by coins corresponding to their value (dimes, nickels, or pennies), and the total cost of the purchase is calculated. A marking chip is placed on any empty space with that total on the gameboard.
2. Players write the number of each animal purchased over the picture of that animal in the appropriate space in the table. For example, if a student purchased two puppies and one goldfish, he or she would write a 2 over the picture of the puppy and a 1 over the picture of the goldfish.
3. Players take turns choosing items and covering squares until one player has three squares in a row horizontally, vertically, or diagonally.
4. If neither player is able to get three squares in a row, the game is a draw.

School Shopping (Mental Math)
1. One player begins by choosing two items to purchase. The cost of those two items is calculated, and a marking chip is placed on any empty space with that total on the gameboard.
2. Each player colors in the items purchased for that turn in the appropriate space in the table.
3. Players take turns choosing items and covering squares until one player has three squares in a row horizontally, vertically, or diagonally.
4. If neither player is able to get three squares in a row, the game is a draw.

Pet Shop

Goldfish
1¢

Puppies
10¢

Kittens
5¢

Shopper One | Shopper Two

1
2
3
4

30¢	11¢	16¢
15¢	3¢	12¢
21¢	16¢	7¢

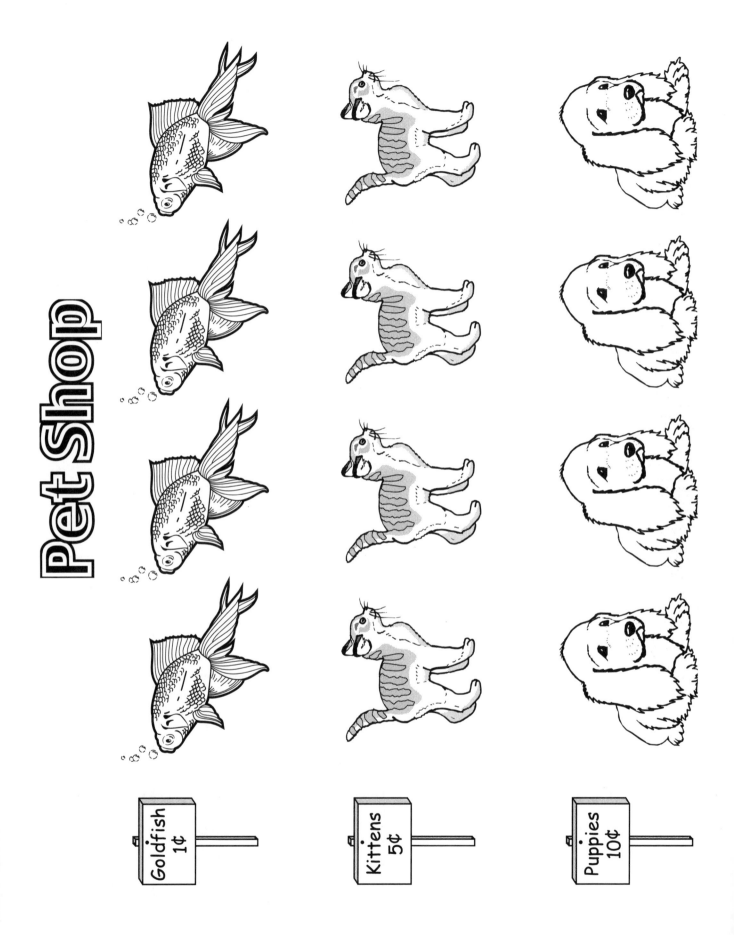

Pet Shop

Goldfish 1¢

Kittens 5¢

Puppies 10¢

School Shopping

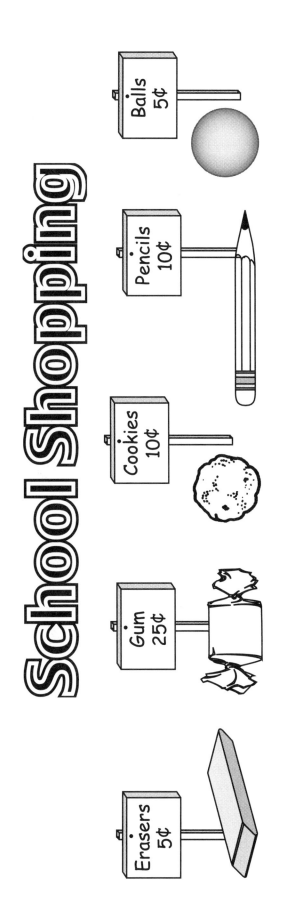

Balls 5¢

Pencils 10¢

Cookies 10¢

Gum 25¢

Erasers 5¢

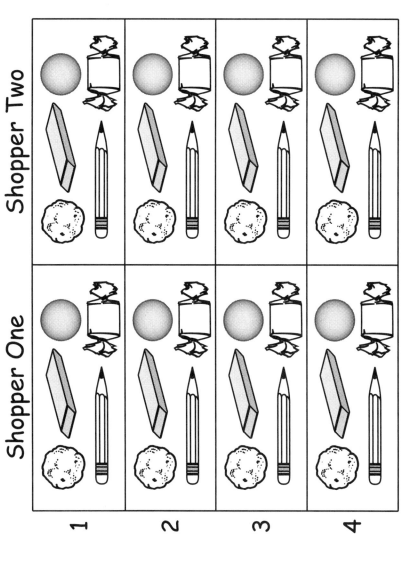

Shopper One	Shopper Two
1	
2	
3	
4	

30¢	10¢	35¢
15¢	20¢	10¢
35¢	15¢	30¢

Roll to a Quarter

Purpose of the Game
Students will roll a die and take the number of each roll in either dimes or pennies. They will try to get as close to 25¢ as they can without going over.

Materials
One die per group
Glue sticks or tape
Scissors
Penny and dime coin strips (see *Management 2*)
Student sheets

Management
1. This game is designed to be played in pairs.
2. You will need to make several copies of the coin sheets included. Begin by giving each pair one strip of dimes and two strips of pennies. (This should be enough to play two or three games, depending on the rolls students get.) As they run out of coins, they can come to you and get more. You may wish to cut out the coins ahead of time or have students do this themselves.
3. Students should use a glue stick or transparent tape to affix the coins to each coin purse/wallet.
4. Students will need one copy of the coin purse/wallet page for each round they play.

Rules
1. One student begins by rolling the die. The number rolled may be taken in either dimes or pennies. For example, if a 2 is rolled, either two dimes (20¢) or two pennies (2¢) may be taken. The exception to this rule is when choosing dimes would make the student go over 25¢. (This means any time a student rolls a 3, 4, 5, or 6, the roll must be taken in pennies.)
2. For each roll, the coins chosen must be glued to the appropriate coin purse/wallet and the total for that roll written in the space provided. For example, if a 4 is rolled, four pennies would be glued to the coin purse/wallet and 4¢ would be written on the *Total* line.
3. Players take turns rolling the die until they have each had five rolls. Before each roll, players must state their current total. If any player's total exceeds 25¢ before five rolls have been taken, that player loses that round, and the game begins again.
4. If a player reaches a desirable total before all five rolls have been taken, he or she may choose to hold. The decision to hold must be made before the player rolls the die and stated out loud as "I freeze." Once the decision has been made, it cannot be reversed, even if the other player gets a higher total.
5. After five rolls, the player who is the closest to 25¢ without going over is the winner.

Variation
Use dimes and nickels and have students roll to a dollar. (You may find that more than five rolls per round are needed for this version of the game.)

ROLL to a Quarter

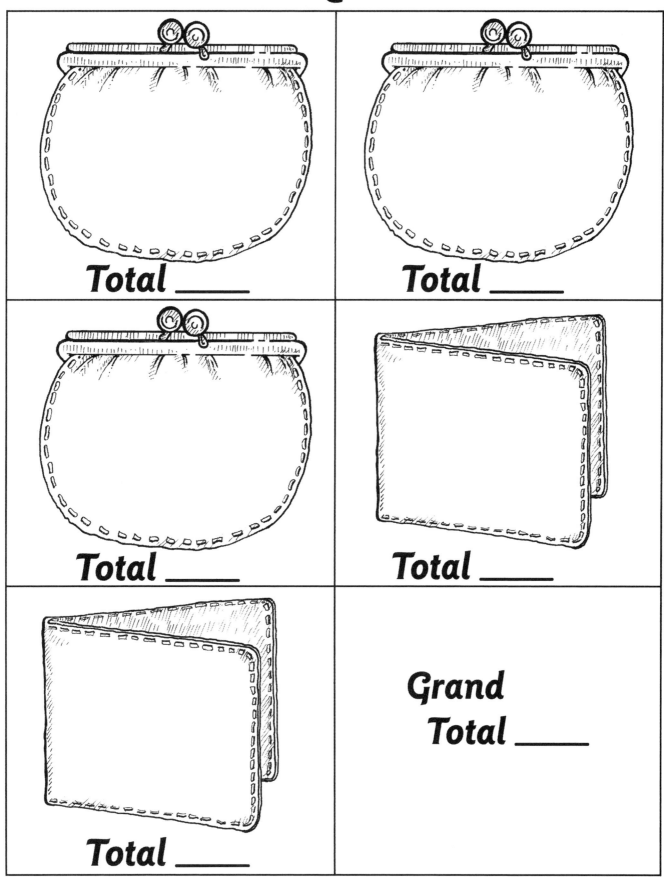

Total _____

Total _____

Total _____

Total _____

Total _____

Grand
Total _____

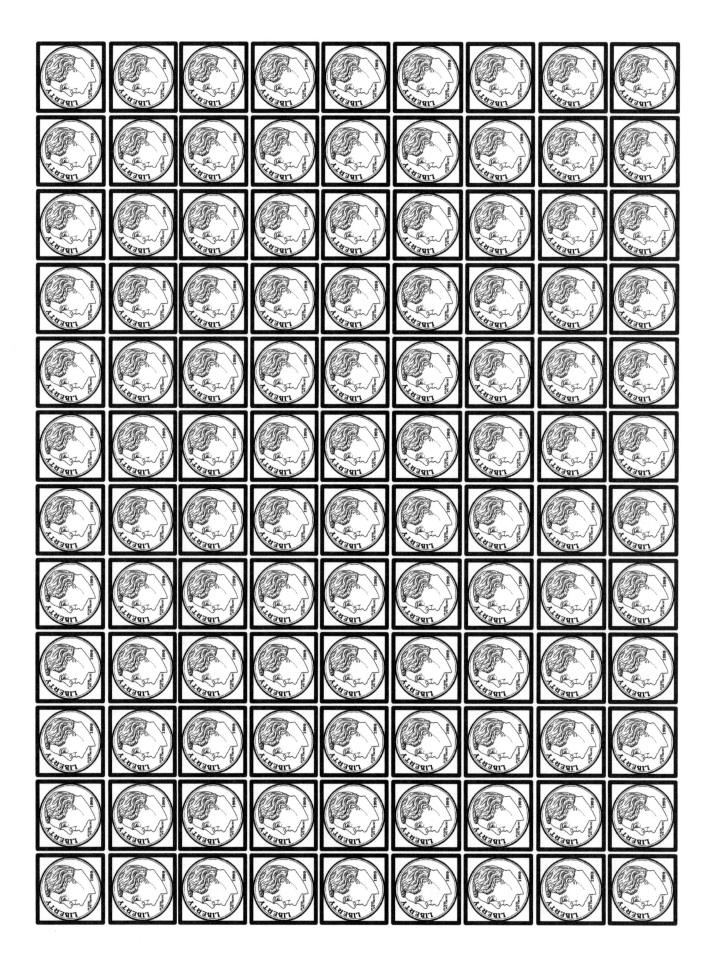

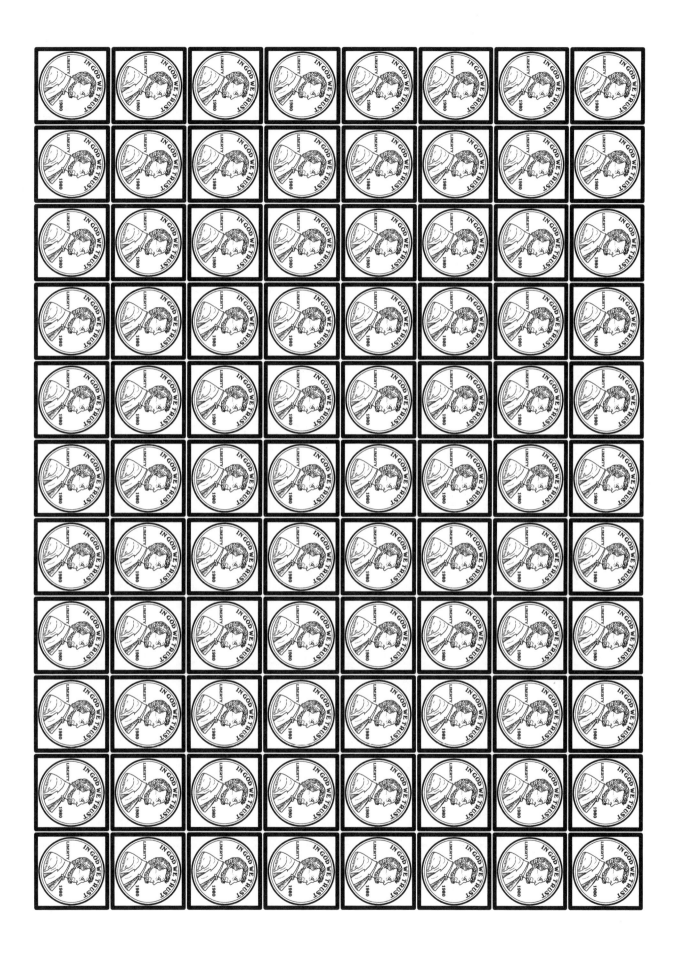

Roll from a Dollar

Purpose of the Game
Students will roll a die and subtract the number of each roll from a dollar in either nickels or dimes. They will try to get as close to 25¢ as they can without going under.

Materials
For each group:
  one die
  set of nickels, dimes, and quarters
    (see *Management 2, 3*)
  cup
  student sheet(s)

Management
1. This game is designed to be played in groups of three. Two students will be players, and a third will be the banker. Students should rotate roles after each round.
2. Each player will need to begin the game with one quarter, four dimes, and seven nickels. Real or play money may be used.
3. The banker will need an adequate supply of nickels and dimes so that the players can trade their coins as needed.
4. Each player will need one copy of the first recording page for each round played. They will also need pencils for making coin rubbings.
5. There is an optional student sheet provided that gives students a table in which to record the specifics of each roll.

Rules
1. To set up the game, each player should place coins totaling $1.00 (one quarter, four dimes, and seven nickels) in the blank space at the top of the first recording page. The banker should have the extra nickels and dimes in a cup or similar container.
2. One player begins by rolling the die. The number rolled may be subtracted from $1.00 in either nickels or dimes. For example, if a 3 is rolled, either three nickels (15¢) or three dimes (30¢) may be subtracted.
3. To subtract a coin, it must be removed from the student page and placed aside. If a student does not have enough of the type of coin he or she wants to subtract, the appropriate number of the other coins must be traded with the banker. For example, if a student begins by rolling a six and

wants to subtract six dimes, he or she would need to exchange four nickels with the banker to receive the two additional dimes necessary.
4. Each turn should be recorded by making a rubbing of the coins removed in the appropriate space at the bottom of the page. If students are using the second recording sheet, they should write the appropriate information in that table after each turn.
5. Players take turns rolling the die and recording their choices until they have each had five rolls. Before each roll, players must state their current totals. If any player's total goes below 25¢ before five rolls have been taken, that player loses that round, and the game begins again.
6. If a player reaches a desirable total in fewer than five rolls, he or she may choose to hold. The decision to hold must be made before the player rolls the die and be stated out loud as "I freeze." Once the decision has been made, it cannot be reversed, even if the other player gets a lower total. The word *FREEZE* can be written in the space where the coins would be recorded.
7. After five rolls, the player who is the closest to 25¢ *without going under* is the winner. If both players have the same amount of money, the game is a draw.

Solutions
A sample of how one student's game might look is shown. Both pages have been completed.

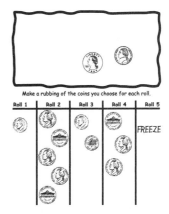

🎲	Number Rolled ⊗	Dimes or Nickels	Starting Amount	Amount Rolled	New Total
Roll 1	1	Dimes	$1.00	10¢	90¢
Roll 2	5	Nickels	90¢	25¢	65¢
Roll 3	2	Dimes	65¢	20¢	45¢
Roll 4	3	Nickels	45¢	15¢	30¢
Roll 5	Freeze				

Make a rubbing of the coins you choose for each roll.

Roll 1	Roll 2	Roll 3	Roll 4	Roll 5

Roll from a Dollar

Number Rolled 🎲	Dimes or Nickels	Starting Amount	Amount Rolled	New Total
Roll 1		$1.00		
Roll 2				
Roll 3				
Roll 4				
Roll 5				

Topic
Patterns

Key Question
What happens to the value of the money you put into *The Magnificent Money Machine*?

Learning Goals
Students will:
1. recognize the number patterns, and
2. solve for the missing addend.

Guiding Document
NCTM Standards 2000*
- *Use a variety of methods and tools to compute, including objects, mental computation, estimation, paper and pencil, and calculators*
- *Illustrate general principles and properties of operations, such as commutativity, using specific numbers*

Math
Number and operations
    addition
    subtraction
Patterns and relationships
Algebraic thinking

Materials
For each group:
    one half-gallon cardboard milk carton
    tagboard, 3" x 12" strip
    money cards (see *Management* 2)
    recording page

Background
The Magnificent Money Machine is used with sets of cards that reflect various number relationships. The amount that appears on the front of each card is related in some way to the amount that appears on the back. In other words, the amount on the front of each card in a set is a certain amount more or less than the number on the back. Each card in the set will have the same rule or relationship.

This activity will give students an opportunity to use money in a problem-solving setting. Younger students can solve the problems by manipulating sets of coins. Older students may think of the problem more algebraically by looking for the patterns using a T-table, recording what went into the machine and what came out.

	IN	OUT
1.	5¢	15¢
2.	7¢	17¢
3.	21¢	31¢

Management
1. Prepare one money machine per group prior to this lesson. This can be done by cutting a 4" x $\frac{1}{2}$" slit across the top and bottom of one side of a half-gallon milk or juice carton. Open the carton to allow your hand inside to guide the 3" x 12" piece of tagboard through the top slit and out the bottom slit. Tape the strip at the top of the carton to hold it in place. Pull approximately an inch of the strip out through the bottom slit and tape it to the carton. When the strip is secure, staple the carton closed.

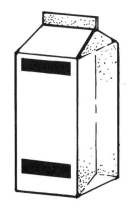 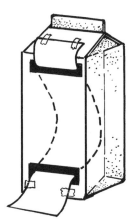

2. Prepare money cards ahead of time on 2" x 2" pieces of tagboard. Put money relationships that you want your students to experience on the cards (example sets have been suggested to get you started). Each set should include three cards. To make sorting easier, make each set of cards a different color. For example, you might write the amounts on the front in blue for plus 5 cents cards, the minus 7 cents in red, and so on. Write all answers on the back in black. The students will then know which side of the card (colors other than black) is placed up in the machine.

Procedure
1. Give each group of students several sets of money cards and one money machine.
2. Demonstrate the proper way to use the money machine. Show students how to place the cards into the machine color side up (colors other than black). Explain that something will happen to the amount on the card as it slides through the machine and out the bottom. Encourage the students to try one of their cards in the machine.
3. Ask the *Key Question*. Have students try the other cards in their set, recording the beginning and ending amounts. Encourage students to identify the *rule* for that set of cards. [Plus 5 cents, etc.] Discuss their discoveries.
4. Ask students to work together to solve each set of money problems. Students that will not be using coins to solve the problems should record the beginning and ending amounts on the recording sheet provided.

Discussion
1. Explain how you solved the problems.
2. Were some problems easier to solve than others? Why or why not?
3. What did you notice about the problems in each set of cards?
4. Create a card that uses the plus 5 cents rule.
5. If I put 10 cents in and get 20 cents out, what is the rule?

Evidence of Learning
Check the students' recording sheets, looking for accuracy in identifying the *rules*.

Extensions
1. Have students create their own sets of money cards to exchange with a partner.
2. Use values over $1.00 in the *Magnificent Money Machine*.

Suggested Cards Sets

Set 1   plus 5¢

Front	3¢	25¢	32¢
Back	8¢	30¢	37¢

Set 2   minus 7¢

Front	11¢	38¢	79¢
Back	4¢	31¢	72¢

Set 3   plus 25¢

Front	50¢	2¢	25¢
Back	75¢	27¢	50¢

Set 4   plus 10¢

Front	7¢	70¢	23¢
Back	17¢	80¢	33¢

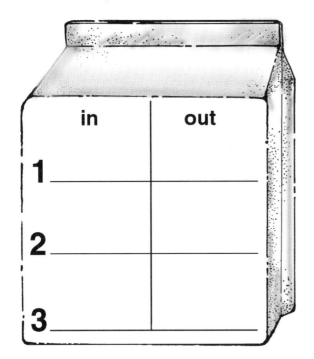

in	out
1	
2	
3	

Color of Cards _____

What's the Rule?_____

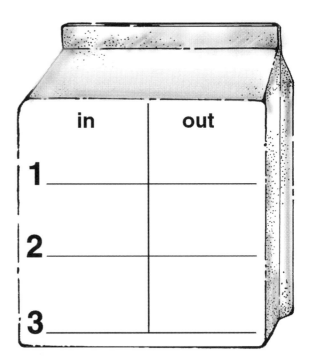

in	out
1	
2	
3	

Color of Cards _____

What's the Rule?_____

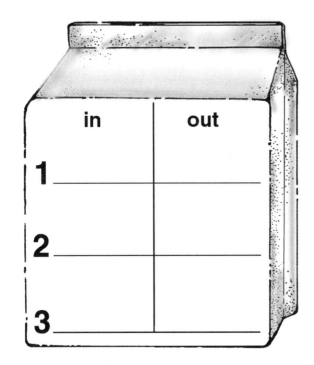

in	out
1	
2	
3	

Color of Cards _____

What's the Rule?_____

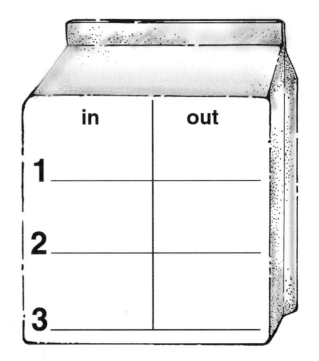

in	out
1	
2	
3	

Color of Cards _____

What's the Rule?_____

Riddle Me This

Purpose of the Game
Students will listen to clues about coin values and record answers in order to earn money.

Materials
For each student:
    Riddle Me This wallets
    recording sheets
    plastic or paper dimes

Management
1. Duplicate and fold a paper wallet for each student. Place one clue in each wallet.
2. Each child will need a wallet, enough dimes for every student in the class, and enough recording sheets to record an answer to each classmate's clue.
3. Each child will read a clue from his or her wallet to the rest of the class. Students receive a dime for each correct answer they record.
4. Set up a classroom store for the students to use their winnings to purchase a snack, a pencil, or other small items.

Rules
1. One student begins by reading the clue in his or her wallet to the class. All other students record the answer to the clue on their recording sheets.
2. Once all answers have been recorded, the reader goes from student to student checking the answers. The reader awards a dime to each student who recorded the right answer.
3. Play continues in this fashion until each student has read his or her clue and awarded dimes to those responding correctly.
4. At the end of the game, winnings may be used to purchase a snack, pencil, or other small item from a classroom store.

1. I have three coins.
   The total value is three cents.
   What coins do I have? [three pennies]

2. I have three coins.
   The total value is fifteen cents.
   What coins do I have? [three nickels]

3. I have three coins.
   The total value is 30 cents.
   What coins do I have? [three dimes]

4. I have two coins.
   The total value is 30 cents.
   What coins do I have? [one quarter and one nickel]

5. I have three coins and none of them are pennies or nickels. I do not have three coins all the same. I have less than 50 cents. What coins do I have? [one quarter and two dimes]. How much money do I have? [45 cents]

6. I have three coins. None of them are the same and I have less than 17 cents, but more than five cents. What coins do I have? [one penny, one nickel, and one dime]

7. I have one coin. It is less than 27 cents and more than 18 cents. What coin do I have? [one quarter]

8. I have one coin. It is less than three cents. What coin do I have? [one penny]

9. I have 75 cents. I have two coins. I do not have two of the same coin. What coins do I have? [one quarter and one half-dollar]

10. I have four coins that are all the same. I have no nickels. The total value of my coins is 40 cents. What coins do I have? [four dimes]

11. I have four coins. Two of my coins are the same. The total value of my coins is 36 cents. What coins do I have? [two nickels, one penny, and one quarter]

12. I have three coins. Two of my coins are the same. The total value of my coins is 55 cents. What coins do I have? [two quarters and one nickel]

13. I have four coins. All my coins are the same. The total value of my coins is 40 cents. What coins do I have? [four dimes]

14. You have 26 cents in the bank. What is the fewest number of coins you could have? Name the coins. [two coins—one quarter and one penny]

15. You have 26 cents in the bank. What is the largest number of coins you could have? Name the coins. [26 coins—26 pennies]

16. There are six coins in the bank and the total value is 15 cents. Name the coins in the bank. [five pennies and one dime]

17. There are nine coins in the bank and the total value is 35 cents. Name the coins in the bank. [five pennies, two nickels, and two dimes]

18. If I have 25 pennies and want to trade them for some dimes and one nickel, how many dimes should I receive? [two dimes]

19. If you order a ten-cent hamburger and a 15-cent milk shake and you have a quarter and two dimes, do you have enough money to pay for your order? [yes]

20. If you order a 30-cent hot dog and a 15-cent soda, and you have a quarter and one dime, do you have enough money to pay for your order? [no]

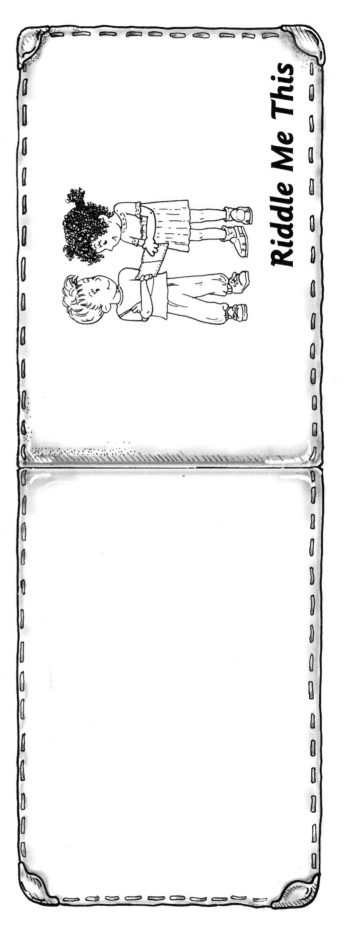

Riddle Me This

Recording Sheet

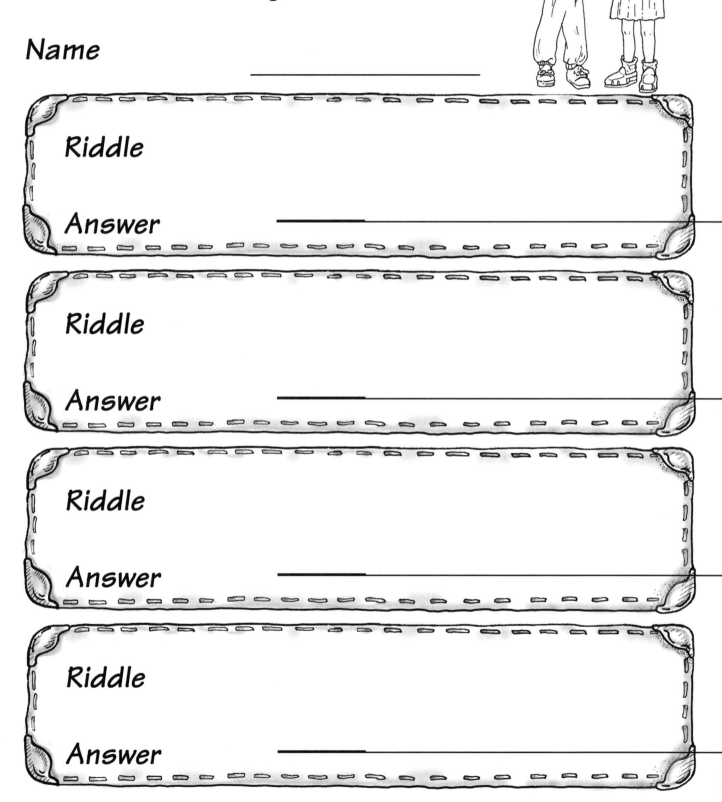

Name _____

Riddle

Answer _____

Riddle

Answer _____

Riddle

Answer _____

Riddle

Answer _____

Topics
Money values
Trading coins

Key Question
How can you represent the total values of the collections of coins using the fewest number of coins possible?

Learning Goal
Students will trade coins to find the fewest number of coins that can be used to represent a specific value.

Guiding Document
NCTM Standards 2000*
- *Count with understanding and recognize "how many" in sets of objects*
- *Develop a sense of whole numbers and represent and use them in flexible ways, including relating, composing, and decomposing numbers*
- *Build new mathematical knowledge through problem solving*
- *Solve problems that arise in mathematics and in other contexts*

Math
Number sense
   counting on
   skip counting
   equivalencies
   trading

Integrated Processes
Observing
Comparing and contrasting
Communicating

Materials
For each student:
   Money In the Bank frames
   plastic bags
   coins (see *Management 2*)
   coin cards
   Money In the Bank Recording Sheet

Background Information
When learning the value of money, young children need to have multiple experiences in making exchanges of one type of coin for another. This lesson provides practice in exchanging different combinations of coins for like values. The students will begin to construct an understanding of coin equivalencies.

Management
1. Prior to the lesson, have the students color and construct piggy bank frames by cutting out the center of the pigs and attaching a plastic bag behind the frame as illustrated.

front

back

2. Gather several pennies, nickels, dimes, quarters, half-dollars, and dollars for each student.
3. Duplicate one coin card for each student in the class.
4. Duplicate a *Recording Sheet* for each student.

Procedure

1. Give each student a piggy bank frame, a coin card, and a set of coins. Ask students to state the total value on their coin cards.
2. Explain that they are to use their coins to represent the total on their cards. The challenge is to represent this total using the fewest number of coins possible. For example, if a student has a coin card with three dimes and four nickels pictured, this value can be represented with a single coin, the half-dollar.
3. Have the students place the coins they have selected into the bag in the piggy bank frames. Ask each student to trade frames with a partner.
4. Instruct the partners to check the frames for accuracy.
5. Once the students have checked their frames for accuracy, have them record the values of their cards and the coins used on the piggy bank *Recording Sheet*. For example, the coin card value may be 35 cents and the coins pictured may be three dimes and one nickel. Students can record the coins they placed in the bags by using coin stamps, by cutting and pasting pictures, or by writing one quarter and one dime, depending on the abilities of the child. They will also need to record the value of the coin card to indicate the target value.

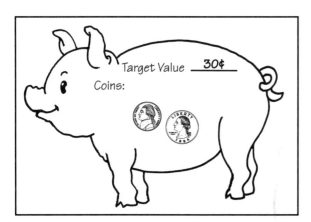

6. Continue until all students have had a chance to change three or four cards.
7. Place a set of coin cards, piggy bank frames, recording sheets, and coins at a center for extended practice.

Discussion

1. Describe the coins you would use to represent 65 cents using the fewest number of coins. [half-dollar, dime, nickel]
2. Describe another combination of coins that equals 65 cents. [two quarters, dime, nickel]
3. Which coin did you use most often in your combinations? Why?
4. Describe two ways to represent 25 cents. Which way uses fewer coins?
5. What is the value of two dimes, one nickel, and three pennies? [28 cents]

Evidence of Learning

1. Look for correct solutions for use of fewest number of coins to represent specific values when students show their work.
2. Listen for accuracy as students describe the coin combinations in their piggy bank frames.

*   Reprinted with permission from *Principles and Standards for School Mathematics,* 2000 by the National Council of Teachers of Mathematics. All rights reserved.

 Coin Cards

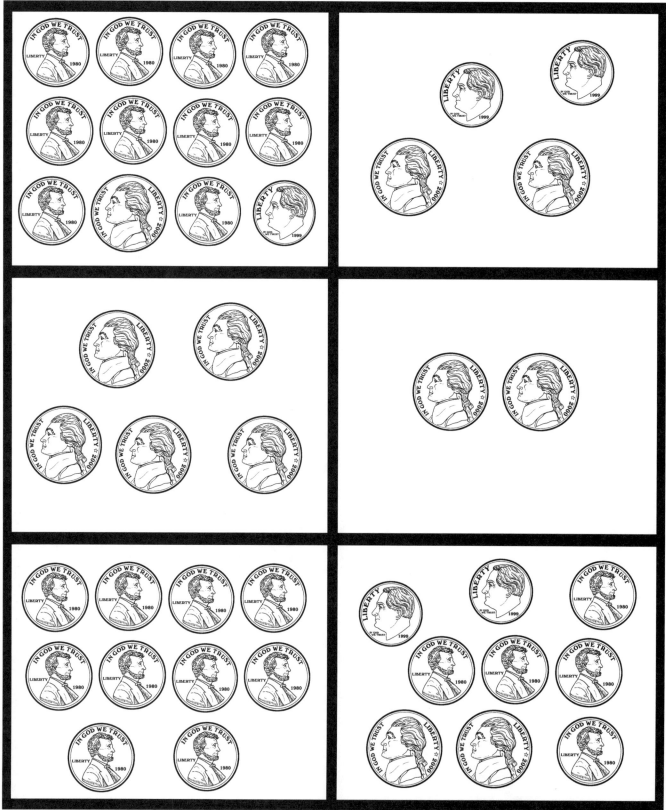

Coin Cards

Coin Cards

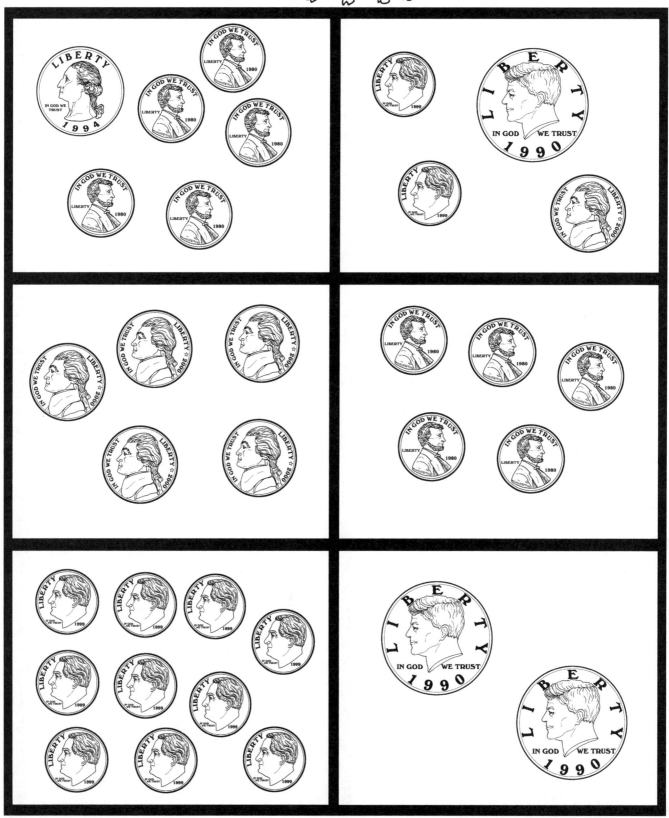

Coin Cards

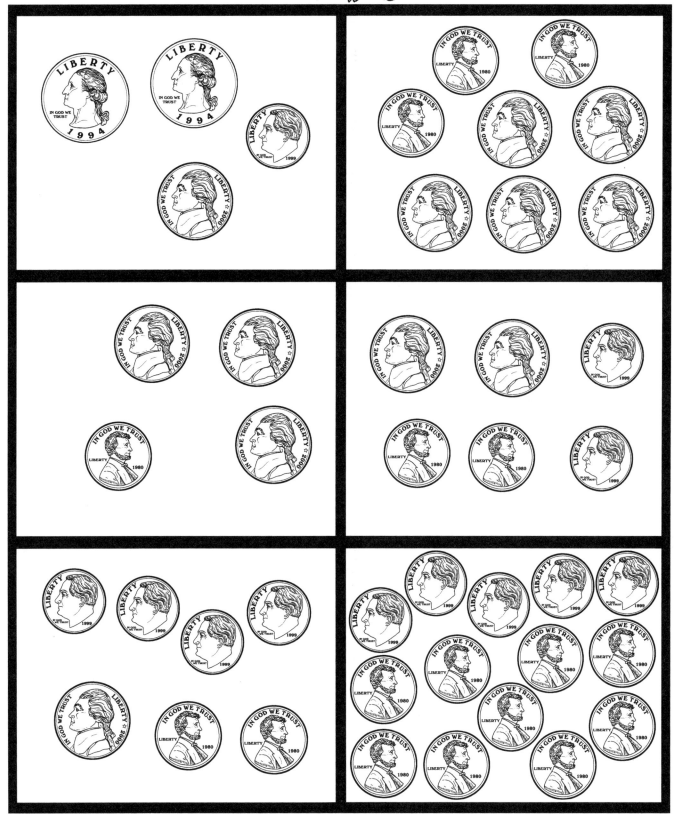

Recording Sheet

Target Value:

Coins:

_____

Target Value:

Coins:

_____

Topic
Money

Key Question
How much will your lunch cost?

Learning Goals
Students will:
1. order from a menu,
2. calculate the total cost of their meal, and
3. determine how much change they should get back.

Guiding Document
NCTM Standards 2000*
- *Count with understanding and recognize "how many" in sets of objects*
- *Connect number words and numerals to the quantities they represent, using various physical models and representations*
- *Understand various meanings of addition and subtraction of whole numbers and the relationship between the two operations*
- *Understand the effects of adding and subtracting whole numbers*

Math
Whole number operations
    addition
    subtraction

Integrated Processes
Observing
Recording
Comparing and contrasting
Communicating
Applying

Materials
Overhead transparency (see *Management 3*)
Pigs will be Pigs by Amy Axelrod
Hot Dog Haven menus and order slips (see *Management 4*)

Background Information
Calculating the total cost of a set of items, whether from a menu or while shopping, is very difficult for young children; determining how much change the customer should get back is even more difficult. However, these skills are necessary because students encounter them in their everyday lives. Children who go to a convenience store need to know that the ten-cent gum and 50-cent drink they wish to purchase will total 60 cents and that they should get 40 cents back from the dollar that they pay the clerk.

For children to be successful adding money and making change, they need to have multiple experiences identifying coins and their values, skip counting, counting on, and counting sets of coins. When these skills are in place, it is important for the children to apply them in playful, real-world contexts. *Hot Dog Haven* will give students an opportunity to apply these skills as they order from a menu, calculate the total cost of their meals, and determine how much change they should get back.

Management
1. Optional: to give the feel of a real restaurant, rearrange the classroom into tables and decorate using a hot dog stand theme.
2. Encourage the students to turn their lined paper sideways; the columns will assist them in lining up the decimals and numbers.
3. Copy the *Hot Dog Haven* order form onto a transparency for demonstration purposes.
4. Each student will need one menu and each pair of students will need several order slips.
5. If your state standards require students to count the change back, take *Part Two* one step further and allow them to count the change back to you.

Procedure
Part One
1. Read *Pigs Will Be Pigs* by Amy Axelrod. (Macmillan Publishing Company. New York. 1994.) Draw the students' attention to the menu found at the back of the book. Discuss the different items listed and their prices. Allow the children to predict what the pigs will order before reading the last two pages of the book.
2. Ask the children if they have ever ordered from a menu.
3. Discuss how the server takes the order, adds up the cost of each item, and gives the customer the bill at the end of the meal.
4. Tell the class that they are going to role-play a restaurant visit. As you welcome the class to the *Hot Dog Haven*, give each student a menu.
5. Discuss the different items on the menu and their prices. Ask the students which of the beverages they could get if they had 50 cents, what kind of dessert they could get if they had 30 cents, etc.

6. Select a student to role-play the part of the customer. Tell the class that you will be the server. Show the student to a table, give him/her the menu and ask what he/she would like to order. Allow the student to order two items from the menu. Record the items ordered and the price of each item on the transparency of the *Hot Dog Haven* order form. Demonstrate how to line up the decimals as you add the two amounts of money together. Allow the students to assist in the computation. Record the total on the order form and give the student the bill.

7. Select another student and allow him/her to order three items from the menu. Record the items ordered and the price of each item. Question the students about the proper way to line up the different amounts of money. Ask the students to assist in the computation. Record the total on the order form and give the student his/her bill.

8. When the students have an understanding of the process of ordering from a menu and calculating the total cost of their meal, assign each student a partner, distribute *Hot Dog Haven* order forms, and allow the students to role-play the process. Instruct them to switch roles and repeat the process several times so that each student has multiple opportunities to order and calculate the cost of the meal.

9. Provide time for the students to share some of their orders and have the class calculate the bills.

Part Two
1. Review the process involved in ordering from a menu and calculating the total bill for the customer.

2. Ask the students to describe how the server knows how much change to give back when you pay your bill. If no one generates the correct response, guide the students to the correct response with questions like, "Will they add the money that you give them to the bill or will they take what you owe them away from the money that you give them?"

3. Select a student to role-play the part of the customer. Give the student two one-dollar bills to spend at your restaurant. Tell the class that you will be the server.

4. Show the student to a table, give him/her the menu and ask what he/she would like to order. Limit the student to two items from the menu. Remind him or her not to exceed two dollars. Record the items ordered and the price of each item on the *Hot Dog Haven* order form transparency for the class to see. Demonstrate how to line up the decimals as you add the two amounts of money together. Invite the students to assist in the computation.

5. Record the total on the order form and give the student his/her bill.

6. Have the student give you the bill and the two one-dollar bills to pay for the meal.

7. Show the students how to record the information on the *Restaurant Bill*. Explain that the server will owe the customer the amount of change listed at the bottom of the page.

8. When the students have an understanding of the process involved in ordering from a menu, calculating the total cost of a meal, and determining how much change there should be, assign each student a partner, distribute *Hot Dog Haven* order forms, and allow the students to role-play the process. Instruct them to switch roles and repeat the process several times so that each student has multiple opportunities to order, calculate the cost of the meal, and determine the correct amount of change due.

9. Have several students share their orders and allow the class to calculate their bills.

Discussion
1. Why is it important to be able to add and subtract money?
2. How do we use money in the real world?
3. How does the server know how much to charge you for your lunch?
4. How much money will your lunch cost if you order _____?
5. If your meal costs $2.50 and you give the server $3.00, how much change will you get back? How do you know?

Extensions
1. Take a field trip to a local restaurant. Allow the children to order from the menu, determine the total cost of their bill, and calculate what change they should get back from a predetermined amount. You may have to make prior arrangements so that the children do not have to work with tax and tip.
2. Bring in menus from local restaurants and allow the children to role-play ordering from the menu, and being the server who determines the total cost of their bill and calculate what change they should get back.
3. Allow the students to create their own menus and exchange menus with a classmate. They can then total each other's orders.

Curriculum Correlation
Axelrod, Amy. *Pigs Will Be Pigs*. Macmillan Publishing Company. New York. 1994.

* Reprinted with permission from *Principles and Standards for School Mathematics*, 2000 by the National Council of Teachers of Mathematics. All rights reserved.

Beverages

Cola	$ .50
Coffee	$ .75
Milk Shake	$1.00

(Chocolate, Vanilla, Strawberry)

Desserts

Pie	$ .30
Cake	$ .40
Cookies	$ .25

Hot Dogs

Hot Dog	$ .60	
Mustard Dog	$ .75	
The Works	$1.00	

(Catsup, Mustard, Onions)

Side Order of Fries	$ .15

Restaurant Bill

HOT DOG HAVEN

MAIN STREET, DOGVILLE

I have _____ . _____

Total bill _____ . _____

Change _____ . _____

Have a nice day

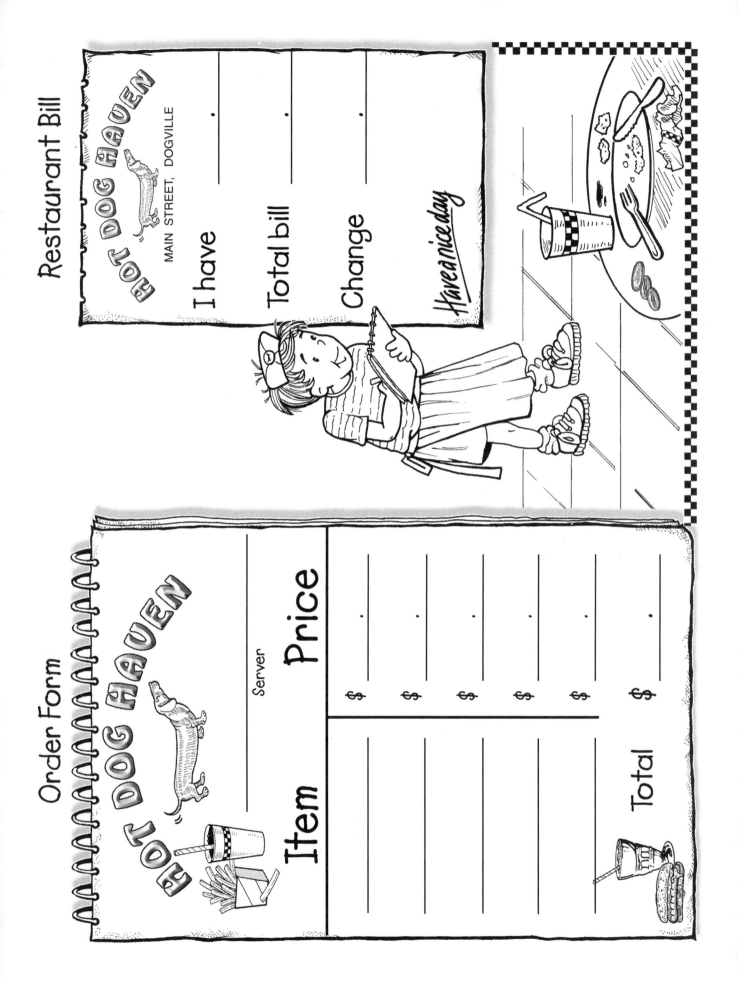

Order Form

HOT DOG HAVEN

Server _____

Item	Price
	$.
	$.
	$.
	$.
	$.
Total	$.

Following are three related experiences that will provide playful practice in
- coin recognition,
- comparing coin values, and
- determining the values of sets of coins.

Shake and Compare

Focus
Students will use a simple game format to identify and compare coins.

Materials
For each pair of students:
    egg cartons (see *Management 1*)
    2 different colored marbles
    scratch paper
    set of coins (see *Management 2*)

Management
1. Use only egg cartons with solid lids. To prepare the cartons, glue one coin into the bottom of each section. Coin stickers or play money can be substituted for real coins if preferred. Ideally each egg carton should contain two copies of each coin (penny, nickel, dime, quarter, half-dollar, Sacagewea dollar), but you can modify the contents to suit the needs of your students.
2. Each group will need a set of coins containing one of each of the coins in the egg carton.

Procedure
Part One
1. Show the class the inside of the egg carton with the coins attached.

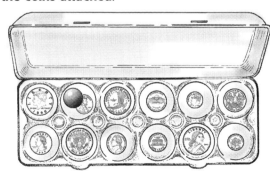

2. Place a marble inside the carton and close the lid.

3. Demonstrate how to gently shake the egg carton allowing the marble to move freely from one section to another.
4. Open the lid and ask students to identify the coin in the section where the marble landed.
5. Ask the students to find the same coin in their sets of coins. Tell them to make a rubbing of the coin on scratch paper and to write the first letter of the name of that coin beside the rubbing to make a record of their work. If appropriate, ask students to record the word.
6. After the demonstration, allow the student pairs to take turns shaking the carton and recording their results.
7. After a designated time, discuss their work. Question them about which coin appeared most often on their paper, etc.

Part Two
1. Give each pair of students an egg carton, two different colored marbles, and scratch paper.
2. Direct students to place both marbles inside their cartons and gently shake the cartons. Ask each of the partners to choose which color marble will be theirs.
3. After shaking the cartons, instruct each pair to open the lid and identify the two coins in the sections where the marbles landed.
4. Ask the students to find the same two coins in their sets of coins. Tell them to make rubbings of the two coins, leaving space between for them to place the correct sign (<, >, or =).
5. Have each student keep a tally of how many times his/her marble landed on the coin of greater value. The player with the most tally marks wins the game.
6. Repeat the game with the winner being the student who most often lands on the coin of lesser value.

Rattle and Count

Focus
Students will determine the value of sets of coins.

Materials
For each pair of students:
    egg cartons (see *Management 1*)
    marbles (see *Management 2*)
    scratch paper
    set of coins (see *Management 3*)

Management

1. Use only egg cartons with solid lids. To prepare the cartons, glue one coin into the bottom of each section. Coin stickers or play money can be substituted for real coins if preferred. Ideally, each egg carton should contain two copies of each coin (penny, nickel, dime, quarter, half-dollar, Sacajawea dollar), but you can modify the contents to suit the needs of your students.

2. Two or more marbles can be used in this game. The more marbles used, the more difficult the game. The marbles need not be different colors.

3. Each group will need a set of coins that includes all possible combinations from their egg carton. For example, if you choose to use three marbles and glue only pennies and nickels in the egg cartons, you would need to include three pennies and three nickels in each coin set since it would be possible for each of the three marbles to land in sections containing the same coins.

Procedure

1. Distribute egg cartons, coins, marbles, and scratch paper to each pair of students.

2. Have one student from each pair place the marbles inside the carton and gently rattle it.

3. After rattling the carton, instruct them to open the lid and identify the coins in the sections where the marbles landed. Instruct them to gather the same coins from their coin sets.

4. Ask the students to determine the combined values of his or her sets of coins and record it on their scratch paper.

5. Have the second student from each pair repeat this procedure.

6. After each student has rattled and counted, ask pairs to compare totals. Have them keep a tally of who has the most money each time. The winner will be the one with the most tally marks.

7. Repeat the game making the winner the one that has the least amount of money each round.

Roll and Count

Focus
Students will count by 1s, 5s, 10s, 25s, and 50s.

Materials
For each pair of students:
   egg cartons (see *Management 1*)
   marble
   scratch paper
   set of coins (see *Management 2*)
   die

Management

1. Use only egg cartons with solid lids. To prepare the cartons, glue one coin into the bottom of each section. Coin stickers or play money can be substituted for real coins if preferred. Ideally, each egg carton should contain two copies of each coin (penny, nickel, dime, quarter, half-dollar, Sacagewea dollar), but you can modify the contents to suit the needs of your students.

2. Each group will need a set of coins that includes six of each coin that you choose to glue into the carton. For example, six pennies and six nickels if you choose to only use pennies and nickels in your cartons.

Procedure

1. Distribute egg cartons, a die, coins, a marble, and scratch paper to each pair of students.

2. Have one student from each pair place the marble inside the carton and gently shake it.

3. After shaking the cartons, instruct the students to open the lid and identify the coin in the sections where the marble landed.

4. Have the students then roll the dice and count the dots to determine how many of that coin they will need to count and record. For example, if the marble landed on the quarter and a student rolled a four, he/she would record 25, 50, 75, and 100.

5. Allow the students to check each other's work as they take turns shaking, rolling, and recording.

Topic
Money

Focused Task
Students will identify how money is part of their daily lives.

Learning Goals
Students will:
1. identify coin combinations that equal the values listed on coupons,
2. compare amounts of money, and
3. identify coins and the one-dollar bill based on clues.

Guiding Document
NCTM Standards 2000*
- *Count with understanding and recognize "how many" in sets of objects*
- *Connect number words and numerals to the quantities they represent, using various physical models and representations*

Math
Number sense and numeration

Integrated Processes
Observing
Recording
Comparing and contrasting
Communicating
Applying

Materials
For the class:
    construction paper
    crayons

Station One
    books about money, both fiction and nonfiction

Station Two
    glue
    coupons
    paper
    pencils
    cups
    coins

Station Three
    riddle cards and recording sheets

Station Four
    glue
    construction paper
    newspapers
    pencils

Station Five
    grocery ads
    glue
    paper
    pencils

Station Six
    store ads
    glue
    paper
    pencils

Background Information
The ability to handle money properly is an essential life skill. While children may earn, save, and spend money, they often lack basic understandings of how money actually works and the careful and responsible management of it. This set of activity stations will allow students to apply money concepts to the real world. They will use coupons to make price

comparisons, helping them become wiser consumers. They will read both fiction and non-fiction books about money to gain a better understanding of our money and the symbols found on it and to see it being used in playful fictional settings. The students will also have an opportunity to see how money concepts are related to other mathematical concepts.

Management

1. Each of the station cards can be used as a whole class activity.
2. There are six stations that should be set up around the room so students can rotate through them one at a time. Twenty minutes should be allotted for each station. A brief description of the stations follows.

   Station One: Students will select and read a book about money.

   Station Two: Students will find the coin equivalents of coupons.

   Station Three: Students will answer money riddles.

   Station Four: Students will find money words and symbols in the newspaper.

   Station Five: Students will compare the costs of products from grocery ads using <, >, and =.

   Station Six: Students will order three products in an ad from lowest price to highest price.

3. Each station will need the materials listed as well as the appropriate station card. Copy the station cards on card stock and laminate for extended use.
4. Provide white copy paper at all stations (except for Station Three) for children to use to record their work.
5. For Station Three, copy the *Riddle Clue Cards* on card stock and laminate. Cut them apart and place them face down at the station. Each child will need a copy of the *Riddle Recording Sheet.*

Procedure

1. Distribute one piece of construction paper and crayons to each student. Invite the students to make and decorate a journal cover. Tell them that they will keep the pages from each station so that the pages can be stapled to the cover to make a journal for all their money work in it.
2. Introduce the money stations that have been placed around the room. Explain the rotation process that will work best in your class setting.

3. Divide the class into groups of three or four students and direct each group to a station. Explain that they will work in each station for 20 minutes at which time you will notify them that it is time to move to the next station.
4. Assist students in stapling the loose pages gathered at the different stations together to form their money journals.
5. When all students have completed the stations, discuss what they did and discovered at each station.

Discussion

1. What kinds of things can you learn about money from books?
2. Why would parents look at grocery ads?
3. Why is it important to compare prices?
4. How were you able to solve the money riddles? Did color clues help? Explain.
5. How do we use coupons?
6. Why is it important to compare prices of products from brand to brand and store to store?
7. How are coupons and the coins that you rubbed beside them related?

Evidence of Learning

1. Look for accuracy as the students combine coins to equal coupon values.
2. Look for correct use of the greater than, less than, and equal to signs as the students compare amounts of money in their journals.
3. Look to see that students correctly identified the coins and the one-dollar bill based on clues that they were given.

*   Reprinted with permission from *Principles and Standards for School Mathematics,* 2000 by the National Council of Teachers of Mathematics. All rights reserved.

Read All About It

1. Choose a book and read.
2. On a piece of paper list the books that you read while you were at the reading center.

Coupons

Materials: glue, coupons, paper, pencil, coins, and cup

1. Choose a coupon from the cup.
2. Glue the coupon onto a sheet of paper.
3. Using coins, show the amount on the coupon.
4. Make a rubbing of the coins on your paper beside the coupon.

Riddles

Materials: riddle clue cards, recording sheets, and pencils

1. Choose a riddle clue card. Read the clue and try to solve the riddle.
2. Record your answer on the recording sheet next to the number that matches the number on the clue card.

Money Collage

Materials: glue, scissors, newspapers, construction paper (9" x 12")

1. Find money symbols, words, and values in the newspaper.
2. Cut them out and glue them onto the construction paper to make a money collage.

Comparing Amounts

Materials: grocery ads, glue, paper, and pencil

1. Cut out two products and their prices.
2. Glue them side by side on your paper with a space between.
3. Use the >, <, and = sign to compare the costs of the items.

Station Five

Ordered Values

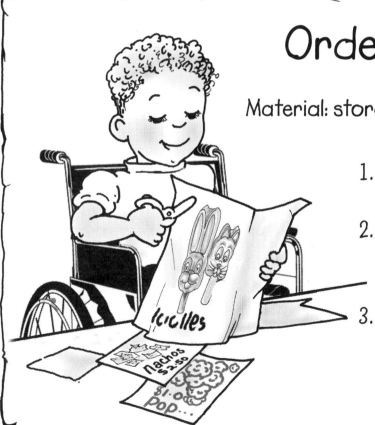

Material: store ads, glue, paper, and pencil

1. Cut out three products and their prices.
2. Put them in order from the lowest price to the highest price.
3. Glue the pictures onto the paper in order and label the lowest priced product.

Station Six

123

Riddle Clue Cards

1.
I am copper.

What am I?

2.
I am green and made of paper.

What am I?

3.
I am worth 25¢.

What am I?

4.
I am the smallest, thinnest coin.

What am I?

5.
I am worth 5¢.

What am I?

6.
I am worth 1¢.

What am I?

7.
I am large and silver and have an eagle on one side.

What am I?

8.
I am silver and have a smooth edge.

What am I?

9.
I am worth 10¢.

What am I?

Name_____

Riddle Recording Sheet

Riddle 1. I am a_____.

Riddle 2. I am a_____.

Riddle 3. I am a_____.

Riddle 4. I am a_____.

Riddle 5. I am a_____.

Riddle 6. I am a_____.

Riddle 7. I am a_____.

Riddle 8. I am a_____.

Riddle 9. I am a_____.

Children's Literature for Money

Adams, Barbara Johnston. *The Go-Around Dollar*. Macmillan Publishing Company. New York. 1992.

Allen, Nancy Kelly. *Once Upon A Dime*. Charlesbridge Publishing. Watertown, MA. 1999.

Axelrod, Amy. *Pigs Will Be Pigs*. Macmillan Publishing Company. New York. 1994.

Chinn, Karen. *Sam and the Lucky Money*. Lee & Low Books. New York. 1997.

Cribb, Joe. *Eyewitness Books, Money*. Alfred A. Knopf, Inc. New York. 1990.

Diggory, Shields Carol. *Lunch Money and Other Poems About School*. Puffin. New York. 1998.

Greene, Stephanie. *Owen Foote, Money Man*. Clarion Books. New York. 2000.

Lanczak, Rozanne Williams. *The Coin Counting Book*. Charlesbridge Publishing. Watertown, MA. 2001.

Leedy, Loreen. *The Monster Money Book*. Holiday House Paperback. New York. 2000.

Murphy, Stuart J. *The Penny Pot*. HarperCollins Publishers. New York. 1998.

Parker, Nancy Winslow. *Money, Money, Money*. HarperCollins Publishers. New York. 1995.

Plumer, David. *Baseball Cards and Piggy Banks*. Creative Teaching Press. Huntington Beach, CA. 2001.

Stewart, Sarah. *The Money Tree*. Sunburst. Wilmington, MA. 1994.

Trapani, Iza. *How Much Is That Doggie in the Window?* Charlesbridge Publishing. Watertown, MA. 1997.

Viorst, Judith. *Alexander, Who Used to Be Rich Last Sunday*. Scholastic, Inc. New York. 1978.

Wells, Rosemary. *Bunny Money*. Puffin. New York. 2000.

Zimelamn, Nathan. *Sold! A Mothematics Adventure*. Charlesbridge Publishing. Watertown, MA. 2000.

The AIMS Program

AIMS is the acronym for "Activities Integrating Mathematics and Science." Such integration enriches learning and makes it meaningful and holistic. AIMS began as a project of Fresno Pacific University to integrate the study of mathematics and science in grades K-9, but has since expanded to include language arts, social studies, and other disciplines.

AIMS is a continuing program of the non-profit AIMS Education Foundation. It had its inception in a National Science Foundation funded program whose purpose was to explore the effectiveness of integrating mathematics and science. The project directors in cooperation with 80 elementary classroom teachers devoted two years to a thorough field-testing of the results and implications of integration.

The approach met with such positive results that the decision was made to launch a program to create instructional materials incorporating this concept. Despite the fact that thoughtful educators have long recommended an integrative approach, very little appropriate material was available in 1981 when the project began. A series of writing projects ensued, and today the AIMS Education Foundation is committed to continuing the creation of new integrated activities on a permanent basis.

The AIMS program is funded through the sale of books, products, and staff development workshops, and through proceeds from the Foundation's endowment. All net income from programs and products flows into a trust fund administered by the AIMS Education Foundation. Use of these funds is restricted to support of research, development, and publication of new materials. Writers donate all their rights to the Foundation to support its on-going program. No royalties are paid to the writers.

The rationale for integration lies in the fact that science, mathematics, language arts, social studies, etc., are integrally interwoven in the real world, from which it follows that they should be similarly treated in the classroom where students are being prepared to live in that world. Teachers who use the AIMS program give enthusiastic endorsement to the effectiveness of this approach.

Science encompasses the art of questioning, investigating, hypothesizing, discovering, and communicating. Mathematics is a language that provides clarity, objectivity, and understanding. The language arts provide us with powerful tools of communication. Many of the major contemporary societal issues stem from advancements in science and must be studied in the context of the social sciences. Therefore, it is timely that all of us take seriously a more holistic method of educating our students. This goal motivates all who are associated with the AIMS Program. We invite you to join us in this effort.

Meaningful integration of knowledge is a major recommendation coming from the nation's professional science and mathematics associations. The American Association for the Advancement of Science in *Science for All Americans* strongly recommends the integration of mathematics, science, and technology. The National Council of Teachers of Mathematics places strong emphasis on applications of mathematics found in science investigations. AIMS is fully aligned with these recommendations.

Extensive field testing of AIMS investigations confirms these beneficial results:

1. Mathematics becomes more meaningful, hence more useful, when it is applied to situations that interest students.
2. The extent to which science is studied and understood is increased when mathematics and science are integrated.
3. There is improved quality of learning and retention, supporting the thesis that learning which is meaningful and relevant is more effective.
4. Motivation and involvement are increased dramatically as students investigate real-world situations and participate actively in the process.

We invite you to become part of this classroom teacher movement by using an integrated approach to learning and sharing any suggestions you may have. The AIMS Program welcomes you!

AIMS Education Foundation Programs

Practical proven strategies to improve student achievement

When you host an AIMS workshop for elementary and middle school educators, you will know your teachers are receiving effective usable training they can apply in their classrooms immediately.

Designed for teachers—AIMS Workshops:
- Correlate to your state standards;
- Address key topic areas, including math content, science content, problem solving, and process skills;
- Teach you how to use AIMS' effective hands-on approach;
- Provide practice of activity-based teaching;
- Address classroom management issues, higher-order thinking skills, and materials;
- Give you AIMS resources; and
- *Offer college (graduate-level) credits for many courses.*

Aligned to district and administrator needs—AIMS workshops offer:
- Flexible scheduling and grade span options;
- Custom (one-, two-, or three-day) workshops to meet specific schedule, topic and grade-span needs;
- Pre-packaged one-day workshops on most major topics—only $3,900 for up to 30 participants (includes all materials and expenses);
- Prepackaged *week-long* workshops (four- or five-day formats) for in-depth math and science training—only $12,300 for up to 30 participants (includes all materials and expenses);
- Sustained staff development, by scheduling workshops throughout the school year and including follow-up and assessment;
- Eligibility for funding under the Eisenhower Act and No Child Left Behind; and
- Affordable professional development—save when you schedule consecutive-day workshops.

University Credit - Correspondence Courses

AIMS offers correspondence courses through a partnership with Fresno Pacific University.
- *Convenient* distance-learning courses—you study at your own pace and schedule. No computer or Internet access required!

The tuition for each three-semester unit graduate-level course is $264 plus a materials fee.

The AIMS Instructional Leadership Program

This is an AIMS staff-development program seeking to prepare facilitators for leadership roles in science/math education in their home districts or regions. Upon successful completion of the program, trained facilitators become members of the AIMS Instructional Leadership Network, qualified to conduct AIMS workshops, teach AIMS in-service courses for college credit, and serve as AIMS consultants. Intensive training is provided in mathematics, science, process and thinking skills, workshop management, and other relevant topics.

Introducing AIMS Science Core Curriculum

Developed in alignment with your state standards, AIMS' Science Core Curriculum gives students the opportunity to build content knowledge, thinking skills, and fundamental science processes.
- *Each* grade specific module has been developed to extend the AIMS approach to full-year science programs.
- *Each* standards-based module includes math, reading, hands-on investigations, and assessments.

Like all AIMS resources these core modules are able to serve students at all stages of readiness, making these a great value across the grades served in your school.

For current information regarding the programs described above, please complete the following:

Information Request

Please send current information on the items checked:

____ *Basic Information Packet* on AIMS materials ____ Hosting information for AIMS workshops
____ *AIMS Instructional Leadership Program* ____ AIMS Science Core Curriculum

Name _____ Phone _____

Address_____
         Street   City   State   Zip

Magazine

YOUR K-9 MATH AND SCIENCE
CLASSROOM ACTIVITIES RESOURCE

The AIMS Magazine is your source for standards-based, hands-on math and science investigations. Each issue is filled with teacher-friendly, ready-to-use activities that engage students in meaningful learning.

• *Four issues each year (Fall, Winter, Spring, and Summer).*

Current issue is shipped with all past issues within that volume.

1820	Volume XX	2005-2006	$19.95
1821	Volume XXI	2006-2007	$19.95
Two-Volume Combination			
M20507	Volumes XX & XXI	2005-2007	$34.95

Back Volumes Available
Complete volumes available for purchase:

1802	Volume II	1987-1988	$19.95
1804	Volume IV	1989-1990	$19.95
1805	Volume V	1990-1991	$19.95
1807	Volume VII	1992-1993	$19.95
1808	Volume VIII	1993-1994	$19.95
1809	Volume IX	1994-1995	$19.95
1810	Volume X	1995-1996	$19.95
1811	Volume XI	1996-1997	$19.95
1812	Volume XII	1997-1998	$19.95
1813	Volume XIII	1998-1999	$19.95
1814	Volume XIV	1999-2000	$19.95
1815	Volume XV	2000-2001	$19.95
1816	Volume XVI	2001-2002	$19.95
1817	Volume XVII	2002-2003	$19.95
1818	Volume XVIII	2003-2004	$19.95
1819	Volume XIX	2004-2005	$35.00

Call today to order back volumes: 1.888.733.2467.

Call **1.888.733.2467** or go to **www.aimsedu.org**

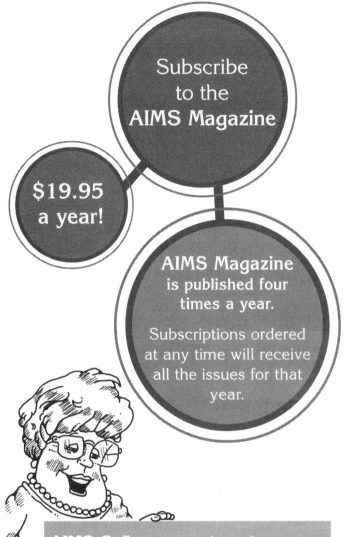

Subscribe to the AIMS Magazine

$19.95 a year!

AIMS Magazine is published four times a year.

Subscriptions ordered at any time will receive all the issues for that year.

AIMS Online – www.aimsedu.org

For the latest on AIMS publications, tips, information, and promotional offers, check out AIMS on the web at www.aimsedu.org. Explore our activities, database, discover featured activities, and get information on our college courses and workshops, too.

AIMS E-News

While visiting the AIMS website, sign up for AIMS E-News, our FREE e-mail newsletter. Published four times per year, AIMS E-News brings you food for thought. Each issue delivers:

• **Thought-provoking articles on curriculum and pedagogy;**

• **Creative ideas on teaching math and science more effectively; and**

• **Sample activities.**

Sign up today!

AIMS Program Publications

Actions with Fractions 4-9
Awesome Addition and Super Subtraction 2-3
Bats Incredible! 2-4
Brick Layers 4-9
Brick Layers II 4-9
Chemistry Matters 4-7
Counting on Coins K-2
Cycles of Knowing and Growing 1-3
Crazy about Cotton Book 3-7
Critters 2-5
Down to Earth 5-9
Electrical Connections 4-9
Exploring Environments Book K-6
Fabulous Fractions 3-6
Fall into Math and Science K-1
Field Detectives 3-6
Finding Your Bearings 4-9
Floaters and Sinkers 5-9
From Head to Toe 5-9
Fun with Foods 5-9
Glide into Winter with Math & Science K-1
Gravity Rules! Activity Book 5-12
Hardhatting in a Geo-World 3-5
It's About Time K-2
It Must Be A Bird Pre-K-2
Jaw Breakers and Heart Thumpers 3-5
Looking at Geometry 6-9
Looking at Lines 6-9
Machine Shop 5-9
Magnificent Microworld Adventures 5-9
Marvelous Multiplication and Dazzling Division 4-5
Math + Science, A Solution 5-9
Mostly Magnets 2-8
Movie Math Mania 6-9
Multiplication the Algebra Way 4-8
Off The Wall Science 3-9
Our Wonderful World 5-9
Out of This World 4-8
Overhead and Underfoot 3-5
Paper Square Geometry:
    The Mathematics of Origami 5-12
Puzzle Play 4-8
Pieces and Patterns 5-9
Popping With Power 3-5
Positive vs. Negative 6-9

Primarily Bears K-6
Primarily Earth K-3
Primarily Physics K-3
Primarily Plants K-3
Problem Solving: Just for the Fun of It! 4-9
Proportional Reasoning 6-9
Ray's Reflections 4-8
Sense-Able Science K-1
Soap Films and Bubbles 4-9
Spatial Visualization 4-9
Spills and Ripples 5-12
Spring into Math and Science K-1
The Amazing Circle 4-9
The Budding Botanist 3-6
The Sky's the Limit 5-9
Through the Eyes of the Explorers 5-9
Under Construction K-2
Water Precious Water 2-6
Weather Sense:
    Temperature, Air Pressure, and Wind 4-5
Weather Sense: Moisture 4-5
Winter Wonders K-2

Spanish/English Editions*
Brinca de alegria hacia la Primavera con las
    Matemáticas y Ciencias K-1
Cáete de gusto hacia el Otoño con las
    Matemáticas y Ciencias K-1
Conexiones Eléctricas 4-9
El Botanista Principiante 3-6
Los Cinco Sentidos K-1
Ositos Nada Más K-6
Patine al Invierno con Matemáticas y Ciencias K-1
Piezas y Diseños 5-9
Primariamente Física K-3
Primariamente Plantas K-3
Principalmente Imanes 2-8

*   All Spanish/English Editions include student pages in
    Spanish and teacher and student pages in English.

Spanish Edition
Constructores II: Ingeniería Creativa Con Construcciones LEGO® (4-9)
    The entire book is written in Spanish. English pages not included.

Other Science and Math Publications
Historical Connections in Mathematics, Vol. I 5-9
Historical Connections in Mathematics, Vol. II 5-9
Historical Connections in Mathematics, Vol. III 5-9
Mathematicians are People, Too
Mathematicians are People, Too, Vol. II
Teaching Science with Everyday Things
What's Next, Volume 1, 4-12
What's Next, Volume 2, 4-12
What's Next, Volume 3, 4-12

For further information write to:
AIMS Education Foundation • P.O. Box 8120 • Fresno, California 93747-8120
www.aimsedu.org/ • Fax 559.255.6396

AIMS Duplication Rights Program

AIMS has received many requests from school districts for the purchase of unlimited duplication rights to AIMS materials. In response, the AIMS Education Foundation has formulated the program outlined here. There is a built-in flexibility which, we trust, will provide for those who use AIMS materials extensively to purchase such rights for either individual activities or entire books.

It is the goal of the AIMS Education Foundation to make its materials and programs available at reasonable cost. All income from the sale of publications and duplication rights is used to support AIMS programs; hence, strict adherence to regulations governing duplication is essential. Duplication of AIMS materials beyond limits set by copyright laws and those specified below is strictly forbidden.

Limited Duplication Rights

Any purchaser of an AIMS book may make up to *200 copies* of any activity in that book for use at *one school site*. Beyond that, rights must be purchased according to the appropriate category.

Unlimited Duplication Rights for Single Activities

An individual or school may purchase the right to make an unlimited number of copies of a single activity. The royalty is $5.00 per activity per school site.

Examples: 3 activities x 1 site x $5.00 = $15.00
           9 activities x 3 sites x $5.00 = $135.00

Unlimited Duplication Rights for Entire Books

A school or district may purchase the right to make an unlimited number of copies of a single, *specified* book. The royalty is $20.00 per book per school site. This is in addition to the cost of the book.

Examples: 5 books x 1 site x $20.00 = $100.00
          12 books x 10 sites x $20.00 = $2400.00

Magazine Duplication Rights

Those who purchase the *AIMS Magazine* are hereby granted permission to make up to 200 copies of any portion of it, provided these copies will be used for educational purposes. Unlimited duplication rights for magazines are $10 per issue or $100 per volume (10 issues).

Workshop Instructors' Duplication Rights

Workshop instructors may distribute to registered workshop participants a maximum of 100 copies of any article and/or 100 copies of no more than eight activities, provided these six conditions are met:

1. Since all AIMS activities are based upon the *AIMS Model of Mathematics* and the *AIMS Model of Learning*, leaders must include in their presentations an explanation of these two models.
2. Workshop instructors must relate the AIMS activities presented to these basic explanations of the AIMS philosophy of education.
3. The copyright notice must appear on all materials distributed.
4. Instructors must provide information enabling participants to order books and magazines from the Foundation.
5. Instructors must inform participants of their limited duplication rights as outlined below.
6. Only student pages may be duplicated.

Written permission must be obtained for duplication beyond the limits listed above. Additional royalty payments may be required.

Workshop Participants' Rights

Those enrolled in workshops in which AIMS student activity sheets are distributed may duplicate a maximum of 35 copies or enough to use the lessons one time with one class, whichever is less. Beyond that, rights must be purchased according to the appropriate category.

Application for Duplication Rights

The purchasing agency or individual must clearly specify the following:
1. Name, address, and telephone number
2. Titles of the books for Unlimited Duplication Rights contracts
3. Titles of activities for Unlimited Duplication Rights contracts
4. Magazine issues and/or volumes for Unlimited Duplication Rights contracts
5. Names and addresses of school sites for which duplication rights are being purchased

NOTE: Books and magazines to be duplicated must be purchased separately and are not included in the contract for Unlimited Duplication Rights.

The requested duplication rights are automatically authorized when proper payment is received, although a *Certificate of Duplication Rights* will be issued when the application is processed.

Address all correspondence to: **Contract Division**
AIMS Education Foundation   www.aimsedu.org
P.O. Box 8120   Fax 559.255.6396
Fresno, CA 93747-8120